The Drag Queens of New York
An Illustrated Field Guide

"My father looked at me and said, 'Ooh what an ugly baby.' Then a woman in a fur coat tapped him on the shoulder and said, 'If you don't want this child I will take him because I just lost mine.' Ever since then I thought to myself, 'Why didn't you give me to her . . . she had a fashion sense.' "

—*HEDDA LETTUCE*

"That ain't a woman—that's a six-foot Crayola box!"

—*CHICKLET (on Miss Understood)*

Julian Fleisher is a graduate of Yale. He lives in New York.

The Drag Queens of New York

of

New York

An
Illustrated Field Guide

by
Julian Fleisher

Pandora
An Imprint of HarperCollins*Publishers*

Pandora
An Imprint of HarperCollins*Publishers*
77–85 Fulham Palace Road,
Hammersmith, London W6 8JB

Originally published by Riverhead Books, New York 1996
Published by Pandora 1997
10 9 8 7 6 5 4 3 2 1

Book design by H Roberts Design
Cover design by James R. Harris
Cover photo credit: Michael Britto, 1996
Cover photo models: The Misstress Formika, Mona Foot, Candis Cayne
Cover make-up artists: Scott English for Mona Foot and John Toth for The Misstress Formika and Candis Cayne
Cover clothing provided by Pat Fieldís
All interior photos by Brooke Williams, 1996, unless noted otherwise.
Interior photo of Charles Busch on page 106 by David Morgan
Interior photos of Lypsinka on pages 139, 141 by Albert Sanchez
Interior photo of the 'Lady' Bunny on page 101 by Tom Pitts
Interior photo of the 'Lady' Bunny on page 103 by Scott Lifshutz

WALK ON THE WILD SIDE
Words and music by Lou Reed
© 1972 Oakfield Avenue Music Ltd
All rights controlled and administered by SCREEN GEMS-EMI MUSIC INC.
All rights reserved. International copyright secured. Used by permission.

A catalogue record for this book
is available from the British Library

ISBN 0 04 440994 X

Printed and bound in Great Britain by
Woolnough Bookbinding Limited, Irthlingborough, Northamptonshire

For Paul

"You better work it out . . ."

ACKNOWLEDGMENTS

Many heartfelt thanks to the following very patient, very tolerant, very helpful souls:

Sara J. Welch, Rocco Debonis and Julie Fendo for their work as faithful research associates, intrepid field observers and good friends, too; Anne Moses, Polly Segal and Mark Voss for their transcriptions, counsel and companionship; Tina Miletich for generosity beyond the call of duty; Paul Franklin, Jeremy Richardson, Kelly Halpine, Pam Yee and Leigh Feldman for their keen readership and constructive criticism early on, and Mary South and Kathryn Crosby for theirs in the end; Hapi Phace and Augusto Muchado for their info and inspiration; and Rikki, Paula, Leon and Adele for everything else, all the time.

CONTENTS

"Whether it be the sweeping eagle in his flight, or the open apple-blossom, the toiling work-horse, the blithe swan, the branching oak, the winding stream at its base, the drifting clouds, over all the coursing sun, form ever follows function, and this is the law."

—Louis Sullivan, Architect

"You better watch it girl! This size twelve, patent-leather, Gucci pump can also be a deadly weapon!"

—The "Lady" Bunny, Drag Queen

PREFACE

In the typically oppressive heat of a late August night in 1984, deep in the heart of New York's infamous Alphabet, several weary, overworked drag queens stumbled out of a cramped night club called the Pyramid and into the shadows of the foul cesspool of Tompkins Square Park. Wobbling drunkenly on tired ankles atop six-inch heels, they commandeered the park's crumbling concrete band shell and in front of a preassembled audience of assorted drug dealers, addicts, homeless families, skinheads and squatters, artists and various other combinations of the above, they put on a show. A spontaneous and surreal explosion of music, theater and lip-syncing, the celebration that grew out of that gathering—which continued throughout the following two days and nights—was christened Wigstock and would be revived every Labor Day, from that day forward.

Twelve years later, that original ragtag assemblage has grown into one of New York's most intensely anticipated, highly attended and, perhaps most importantly, well-covered annual events. What at first conjured up but a handful of the denizens of a New York nether region that terrified most other citizens, now attracts literally tens of thousands of enthusiastic spectators and dozens of performers. The same festival that would as often as not end in a confrontation with the police, today finds—in a Felliniesque turnaround—the Manhattan borough president fighting her way through crowds of celebrity VIPs, duly accredited members of the media, publicists, groupies, fashion designers, record label executives and a dizzying array of spotlight-starved, glamour-crazed queens, to ascend to the stage and present Wigstock's founder and current impresario, The "Lady" Bunny, with an official, city-ordained proclamation that this day be called Wigstock Day in New York City.

The Drag Queens of New York have arrived.

Why a Queen?

$\mathcal{W}$atching drag is a lot like bird-watching. Observing and learning about the lives of queens involves tracking subjects, noting particular habitats and marveling at the diversity of life in the ever-shifting ecosystem of drag in the big city. There are various subspecies to discover and plumage that changes with the seasons. One slowly comes to learn who dominates whom, where in the jungle new queens emerge and who belongs on the list of endangered species. Essentially, the copy from any episode of *Nature* could be applied wholesale to drag in New York, and it would be hard to tell the difference: only late into a graphic description of the giant helmet beetle might it become clear that they were *not* discussing Barbra Streisand's pre–*Funny Lady* hairstyle.

Like birding, however, "dragging" can be laborious and frustrating. While New York is a uniquely fertile drag environment, it is also unforgiving, unpredictable and thick with flora that obscures the fauna. As is it with all highly specialized creatures who depend completely upon a single, fragile niche for survival, queens can come and go in a flash. Others hang around for years and never really catch fire. Some who are "genius" simply quit or get lost just as they are about to hit. Still others disappear for months on end, seemingly gone

The Call of the Wild: A Drag Queen Round Table

With The "Lady" Bunny, Chicklet, Hapi Phace, Miss Understood, Flloyd, Linda Simpson and the author as moderator.

Part I: Civilians

Julian: Let's start by talking about how you relate to civilians when you're working.

Bunny: "Civilians" meaning people who don't do drag?

Julian: People like me, yes.

Miss Understood: It depends how they approach you. You get all these drunk, crazy peo-

forever, only to reappear as suddenly as they vanished. From year to year, the dramatis personae on the steep rake of the Manhattan drag queen stages changes as fitfully as do the venues in which they appear. This field guide is therefore, by necessity, *representative*. Given the mercurial nature of the world in which queens work, there was little chance of catching glimpses of *every* player who passes behind those footlights. In the end, choices about which queens to include were made according to a simple set of measures that any bird watcher might employ in an unexplored locale; a calculus of time, place, and personality that yielded very particular results. For the most part, though, the queens included were all members of the following three basic groups:

1. DRAG STARS. Queens who have succeeded in making names for themselves over a sustained stretch of time. To miss them would be to go to Athens and not notice the Parthenon. They lead the pack. They're old.

2. UP AND COMERS. Queens who, while not yet genuine stars, exhibit all the telltale markings of big ones. Theirs are the names that are beginning to show up more and more often and have begun to amass large groups of faithful fans and hangers-on.

3. WORD OF MOUTH QUEENS. To rely exclusively on one's own taste and experience, except in rare cases, would be to yield a completely unrepresentative survey. Whether famous or not, those queens who—for one reason or another—were consistently cited by *other* queens as worth pursuing proved, across the board, to be the ones most worth seeking out.

In the same way that a seasoned bird-watcher may spend a lifetime following the song of one or two particular species, only to miss ever actually spotting them, this survey was conducted over a six-month period during which several important and interesting queens had dropped out of sight or left town. These include such beloved performers as **Faux Pas** and **Flotilla De Barge**. Others were in town but, like the elusive figures in a jungle painting by Rousseau, they remained unseen or emerged only at the last minute. These include **Paige** (John Waters's favorite New York drag queen),

ple who just come up to you and slobber all over you. Bunny acts retarded to chase them away.

Bunny: And they're so much like yourself.

Miss Understood: No, I think it's really funny the way you act retarded to chase them away. It does work.

Hapi Phace: "Act?"

Bunny: There's this friend of mine in Atlanta, and she would say, "Woooooo!" whenever she got

bored. That just means "Conversation is over but I'm going to leave you thinking"—it's Lady Claire—"leave you thinking that I'm really excited by the whole exchange." And I got that from her. But you can do anything you want that just makes them think, "This person is having so much fun that I can't really stop to talk to bore them." Just like Lahoma. Lahoma is so sweet that you cannot get her out of a club. If you say, "Okay, we're all ready," she's got to stop and say good night to every single person in the club.

Shequida, **Co Co Peru**, **Cybil Bruncheon** and the elusive **Christian Womyn**. Still other queens simply wished to be unavailable—often the most famous of queens. **Lypsinka**, undisputed master of her craft, is mortified by the word "queen" and lives in terror that her image will be reproduced without retouching. **RuPaul**, perhaps the ideal subject for such a book as this, has published her own detailed account of her success, rendering her story not irrelevant, but perhaps redundant. Unfortunately, it's a problem endemic to drag that queens who are reported to be extraordinary are sometimes impossible to locate or communicate with. Ultimately, though, the selections that resulted in this particular group of stories were largely arbitrary and reflect this writer's own tastes, inclinations and various saturation points. There are queens who might well have been a part of the survey who were not.

The profiles are for the most part based on the queens' own tales of their lives. Each one completed an overly long survey (except for **The "Lady" Bunny**, who couldn't be bothered) and sat for interviews during which they highlighted those parts of their lives worth highlighting. Many of their stories overlap, share common elements and were clearly being sugarcoated for the sake of general consumption. By her own estimation, the average queen considers her work to be just this side of selling Girl Scout cookies. For this writer, who is particularly interested in the notion of inventing one's own image, the impulse to explode these personal mythologies is minimal. More compelling is to observe how a queen's life story (as she tells it) tends to complement the visual character she's come up with in drag. (It's a phenomenon not unlike a dog looking like its owner.) Objectivity, while not completely worthless, is only one of several principles worth adhering to when talking trash with your local drag queen. Where it seemed of particular interest—or when a subject's story was directly contradicted by virtually every other queen who would talk—that information was worked into the profile. It should be noted that almost to a queen, the girls refused to dish one another. Aside from the institutional bitchiness that is as much a part of drag as is stocking up on industrial strength under-eye concealer, the drag queens of

Flloyd: Lahoma's the one that started "Yay, girl, yay!" I took that from her. When people grab you in a club and they're trying to talk to you, you go, "Yay, girl, yay!" and just keep walking.

Miss Understood: Well, there's nothing wrong with speaking to us, like I said—

Hapi Phace: Just hand us a twenty-dollar bill before you begin.

Miss Understood: No, but people project upon you. Like they don't even know you and they start coming up and telling you about their ex-wife and their scabies. They just start blathering to you.

Bunny: When did you see Faux Pas?

Miss Understood: When you're in drag you're being looked at by a hundred people at once, so everyone feels that you're ignoring them because you can't stop to talk to everyone at once. You know, I think most drag queens are pretty personable when they're out.

New York don't shit where they eat—exept for **Flloyd**, who rather likes to make a habit of it. Yes, they bust each other's chops relentlessly, and oh how they'll whine about so-and-so when she's not in the room, but for the most part queens are a remarkably united lot: friendly, sororal and anxious to maintain the integrity of their society. Birds of a feather and all.

There is a point at which ornithological similes no longer fly. The humanity of these stories is not meant to be undercut or diminished by one writer's particular perspective or overweening desire to extend a metaphor. The world of New York drag is sprawling, labyrinthine, enigmatic and hilarious. Understanding it all would take the patience of a saint, the dedication of Audubon and enough coffee to keep Juan Valdez in silk and satin for a hundred years. Drag is also disorienting. To become truly familiar with its queens and their unique flair for dramatizing life's absurdities is to have one's perspective changed dramatically. Fear the man whose worldview remains unchanged after fifty or so dinners with the drag queens of New York. To those who gave freely of their stories, then, a word of thanks. To the absent, well, maybe next time.

Hitting the Trail: Some Words to the Wise

Dragging, trawling for queens, throwing out your drag net—call it what you will. When you go looking for drag, here are some things to remember:

1: Finding queens in the first place can be a challenge. To use the parlance of real estate brokers: "Follow the Gays!" With few exceptions, drag remains a queer form of entertainment that attracts a largely gay audience. Even as American culture as a whole becomes more and more gay literate, it can be hard to find drag outside of gay establishments. Check out local gay papers and magazines to get the ball rolling. Once it starts, it won't stop.

2: Oddly, my dictionary gives at least ten different definitions for the word "queen," including "*slang*: male homosexual." But it stops short of the subtly nuanced meaning in which, used as it is by queens as a suffix,

Bunny: Yes, I think so too.

Linda Simpson: But the people that I relate to more in drag are other drag queens. I think everyone else is great, but the people that, you know, you tend to relate to more are the other queens. But don't you?

Hapi Phace: Well, I don't know. Are you working when that's the case?

Linda Simpson: I always search for other queens. I mean, we have something in common.

Bunny: That's not really an answer to the question of how a civilian should approach us. Now, I'll tell you one thing that does happen a lot and is really irritating. And it's not the kind of thing that you always mind, but it's this kind of thing that if you are in not the greatest of moods, can flip your lid: Because you're a drag queen and you're out and you're a hired party girl, you're public property.

"queen" connotes someone with a defining attraction to a particluar type of person or thing. For example, someone who enjoys, say, Latin lovers is called a "Salsa Queen." (Depending on the delivery, this can come off as either deeply affectionate or virulently racist.) Likewise, someone who fills their personal computer with hundreds of RAM-hogging typefaces might be called a "Font Queen," etc. In this way, a "drag queen" can be not only someone who does drag but also someone who enjoys it as a spectator. Or it could mean a person who is sexually attracted to drag queens—"trannie chasers" as they are known in the business—a "Queen Queen" in other words. Whichever, simply make sure to keep track of which is which.

3: Making contact: Many queens have a natural, and probably healthy skepticism for anyone who takes an unusually strong interest in them. Given that they're forever fending off any number of ill-intentioned creeps who would attack them, use them sexually or just want to touch their wigs, queens understandably like to keep their contact with "civilians" somewhat formal and out in the open. New York queens, especially, have developed elaborate systems of defense to keep these nefarious stalkers at bay—unless they're cute. And ultimately, they ask themselves, why would anyone want to get so close as to destroy the mystery and theatricality of their craft. In other words, they don't spend two hours getting done up just to go out and act like one of the guys. Therefore, respect the artifice of it all. Flattery will go far, but just as dogs can smell fear, no one can sense insincerity like drag queens.

4: The little matter of whether to use male or female pronouns is not cut-and-dry. Most queens use female language as a matter of habit, and it's generally safe to follow suit, especially when they're in drag. It can seem strange at first—calling a he a she—but eventually it feels all too right. Out of uniform, though, all bets are off, as the rules change from man to man and from situation to situation. As it turns out, most queens could care less whether you call them him or her, as long as you call them . . . and don't ask their age.

5: If you plan to meet a queen outside of work, be prepared to be stood up. In the dream world of New York drag, the fantasy of celebrity is played

And so they can touch your wig. They can lift your skirt up. That's the most common thing.

Hapi Phace: Right. They grab your tits and they go, "Oh, are these real?"

Bunny: And if you're not in the mood for that, you really can turn around and smack 'em. I mean, you *want* to.

Flloyd: Being touched by strangers, yeah. Weird.

Julian: You mean gay men do that?

Bunny: Oh, gay, straight, girls—

Flloyd: Everyone and everybody.

Hapi Phace: Everybody.

Bunny: It doesn't make any difference at all. That happens all the time.

Hapi Phace: That's the most common way that most people do approach queens.

out to the fullest. Inasmuch as glamour and desirability are at the heart of the drag queen dream, not being able to be bothered is a natural part of the plan. In the same way that her fake boobs say "bust line!," a queen's busy schedule, full dance card and habitual tardiness fairly scream "popular!" If you thought getting Streisand on the phone was tough, try reaching **The Misstress Formika**—unless you're cute.

Also, there's an undeniable tension between the irony that drag queens practice and the earnestness with which they perform. For every queen who tries self-consciously to frame her work as social criticism, political activism or just harmless recidivism, there are at least as many others who just love to dress up. These dualities are rampant within drag; the narcissism and theatricality that drive most queens toward the footlights are as adolescent as can be, while their archness, sophistication and style are products of an almost unparalleled worldliness. Which face a queen will give you is anybody's guess. The most sophisticated of queens may turn out to be just a big baby, like **The "Lady" Bunny,** while the silliest of pranksters turns out to be a keen observer and refined thinker, like **Chicklet**. Be prepared for either eventuality.

6: Above all, drag is meant to be fun. If you're not having any, try again later. It can be disorienting and bizarre. It asks as much of the viewer as it does of the queen. At its best, drag reveals a treasure trove of secret information about how all of us get through the day, get into costume, rehearse our lines and play our parts, so don't be shy about asking questions. Is there a connection between fabulousness and narcissism? (You betcha!) Ever wonder where Linda, Christie and Naomi learned to walk that walk? Wanna know why drag queens have better legs than most seasoned showgirls? Ever care why you care? Go ahead and ask. Let the pros spell out the difference between grinning your way through cocktails and turning the world on with your smile. Self-activation is the Emerald City of this curious journey. Find out how to click your heels even when they're six inches off the floor. And pay no attention to that man behind the curtain.

Bunny: Now, you should be in the mood for that if you're a party hostess at a club.

Hapi Phace: They grab your tits . . .

Bunny: Yes, grab your tits.

Hapi Phace: "Are these real? Are these real?" I mean, how many millions of times do they ask that? "Are these real?"

Flloyd: It's because you're the entertainment. You're the circus clown.

Miss Understood: But they don't realize that what you're wearing could be delicate. I mean, you can't just yank on a wig. It's on my head. I've kicked people really hard for doing that.

Linda Simpson: There's another extreme too. When you're walking on the street or at a club and you're all done up and you look great, and people *ignore* you. Like they're too cool to even acknowledge you. I hate that.

Bunny: Of course, that's actually when you're

Attack of the Fifty-Foot Drag Queen

Why drag, why now, why New York? After all, drag is not new. The arguably fine art of putting on the ritz by putting on the tits is at least as old as recorded history. What's so surprising is that it has taken so many millennia for drag to get any real airtime. True, all things come to those who wait, but who knew the payoff would be so big? At this, the dawning of the age of fabulousness, drag queens are leading the parade—and not just any drag queens. While the current rise of this singular sensation is undeniably international, the nexus of the movement, god bless it, is New York City. And not a moment too soon. Now that Broadway is dead and the Mets are a lost cause, New York is needy for some entertainment of which to be the capital. Yes there is art, yes there is The Dance and now, with the recent advent of the tents, even fashion, but let's face it: NYC ain't what it used to be. Most of what one used to be able to find only here can now be found (virtually) anywhere and often in better form. But now, thankfully, we have our drag queens. Increasingly ubiquitous fixtures in nearly every ring of the Big Apple circus, queens add vim, vigor and, most of all, glamour to any vital function.

Of course, there are drag queens in other cities around the nation, nay,

imagining that you're looking great, but you're looking so horrible—

Linda Simpson: Not me! Not me! But you know what I mean? There's a happy medium, I think, where people acknowledge you and they're friendly and stuff, but polite still.

Flloyd: There are extreme reactions because when you're in drag people don't treat you normally. It's not like "Oh, hey, how's it going?" If they're strangers.

Chicklet: Well, you know, I've been chased up the street leaving cabs and followed and harassed by people, and I love it. And as far as people touching me—

Linda Simpson: Harassed, you like?

Chicklet: I like the harassment slightly, 'cause I live on that danger thing. I was go-go dancing at Tunnel once, up in the crow's nest, and I'm climbing down the ladder, and this guy, like, reached up *into my skirt*. I actually ended up kicking one

around the world. But, like the Sears Tower, the *Chronicle* and the Red Sox, well . . . close but no cigar. Despite its slightly crestfallen bearing, New York is still the ultimate proving ground of the world's creative spirits. Its primacy in the global culture market remains, miraculously, intact. To make it here is still to make it anywhere and this is no less true for the drag queen. There are plenty of queens in San Fransisco and L.A., but the New York scene had already been in full swing by the time either of those questionable fault lines had even been settled. Drag in New York is drag at its best; a centuries-old tradition, with its own iconography, its own vernacular and its own sacred sights.

Most of these treasures have remained buried, however, until very recently. New York recovered slowly from the shock of the **Stonewall** Rebellion and has only gradually given up the fruitless denial of its gay identity; it has likewise been cruelly slow to grant its drag queens the royal treatment they so richly deserve. What's more, these heroes of the gay liberation movement have had to suffer rejection by the very people they liberated. Organizers of various gay pride events are still anxious to keep drag queens as deep in the closet as possible. Their role in **Stonewall** notwithstanding, drag queens, it is argued, serve only to disgust and alienate contemporary onlookers and further the notion that all "these people" are freaks—sad, effeminate clowns who achieve a sense of satisfaction by, at best, engaging in a distasteful display of flamboyance, or, at worst, dressing as women. It is no surprise that, as the outward expression of qualities most everyone would prefer not to think about, drag queens are reviled and pitied to the extent that they are. Any group bucking hard for admittance into the mainstream might well feel compelled to try to disassociate itself from characters such as the Drag Queens of New York. Even the perennially liberal Big Apple has had a hard time enfranchising this particular population.

of his teeth out. So as far as being public property, it's cute to look, but please don't touch. That's what I have to say.

Bunny: Sometimes you don't care if they lift your skirt up. But if you've got hose on that are full of runs and safety pins and your panties are safety-pinned to 'em and there's a big shit stain on them and they're ripe, and they're yellow in the front and brown in the back—

Flloyd: And the gerbil is coming out.

Bunny: —sticking his head out, and he wants you to fix the wheel in there. . .

Julian: Well, then let me ask you, what's your favorite kind of work?

Bunny: Go in, do a show—

Miss Understood: And leave!

Bunny: —and get *paid* and leave! No, that's awful. I mean, you know, have it go well, you know, then hang out afterwards. But one of the

But the times they are a changin'. Something's blowin' in the wind. You just can't keep a good mode of cultural transgression down. And so, with an astonishing alacrity, the drag queens of New York have claimed this century's final decade as surely as the great robber barons claimed that of the last. Like it or not, our insatiable *fin-de-mille* appetite for glamour and idealism dictates that no stone be left unturned as we scour the landscape in search of new icons to adore and consume. When the demand for stars in the heavens has finally outstripped the supply, queens rush in to counteract the deficit. Those who but yesterday were reviled as monsters are now de rigueur at any club, party or opening night.

How? When? Why on earth? Who believes it? I, for one, never liked drag much. Eschewing the apocalyptic prophesies attached to drag by so many, however, I maintained the more typical stance that while it could be amusing in certain contexts, as a rule drag was just unseemly and embarrassing. Not long ago, however, I found myself in a dark East Village boîte, the **Pyramid**, attending a live production of a parody of a Spike Lee film called *Lesbian Jungle Fever*. Don't ask how or why. The point is I liked it. I didn't expect to, of course, but I was genuinely entertained. Little did I know at the time, however, that this was precisely the point. It was during this performance that I underwent the sort of transformation that I would later realize is—and has been for centuries—the very raison d'être of drag. Throughout the history of literature, from Shakespeare to Wilde, from Bugs Bunny to Bashevis Singer, gender play has always served as an instrument of transformation, not only for those who are overtly transformed by the cross-dressing itself, but also, and perhaps more importantly, for those with whom the drag queen comes into contact. Virtually every culture tells stories of confused and disconsolate people (often lovers) who after having encountered and perhaps come to love a drag queen—or after having gazed into the strange mir-

most hateful things is to have to hang out before a show when your mind is, perhaps, on doing something new, or you're not certain how everything's going to turn out—

Flloyd: And there's nowhere to hide—

Bunny: And there are reservations with the sound person or the lighting person, but you have to do the "Hi, Hi, Hi" thing. That's when I get bitter and crabby.

Miss Understood: And sometimes people don't understand that you have to do a show and you're not being rude. Like when I would ask people to leave the dressing room, they'd all ignore me or look at me like I was crazy. When you're doing a show, it's not that easy. I mean, you have to get it together a little bit.

Flloyd: And then afterwards, at the Gatien Corporation, waiting till 5:30 to get paid. That's really annoying.

Ruth Messinger
Manhattan Borough President

The three years that [*Wigstock*] was in Union Square Park was a hassle and a half. But again I want to be clear. Of course some people were motivated by "What is this odd thing, and if it has to exist, leave it over there on avenue B." But there was also a very *real* issue which is *Wigstock*-specific: there were a huge number of holes in the grass in Union Square Park. There were an awful lot of people wearing very high heels. They tore up the entire park. It's always hard to sort that one out. I believe my constituents when they say that this place looks like some kind of lunatic army played golf here. So these are complicated issues . . .

ror of their own transgendered persona—uncover the vital part of themselves that eventually leads to their redemption.

Whether it is Dustin Hoffman as Michael Dorsey in *Tootsie*, who professes to have learned how to be a man only after dressing as a woman, James Garner as King in *Victor/Victoria*, who learns how to love a woman only after having believed he was loving a man, or the many confused lovers in Shakespeare's *A Midsummer Night's Dream*, who uncross their wires only after having had them coyly yanked by the oddly gendered troupe of wood nymphs and fairies, literature has always known that drag's unique power to confuse and reassemble the elements of desire is one of the most powerful narrative tools available. Whether our hero is walking down the yellow brick road, fumbling through the Forest of Arden or spending the night in bed with Jaye Davidson, a Walpurgisnacht is a Walpurgisnacht is a Walpurgisnacht. The difference, however, is that one night with a queen is worth at least several of either of the other options. You do the math: drag is potent . . . and quick.

What's more, the unique power that drag has to shake and bake the average sleeping beauty stems directly and specifically from its transgressive nature. After all, pissing off Daddy has always been the quickest route to transformation. The fact that drag rubs up against our most jealously guarded identity markers, the codes we employ to recognize one gender or

Bunny: And getting paid with a check.

Miss Understood: Hoping it cashes.

Bunny: And not having any screwups in the bookkeeping so that when you actually do wait a week for the money, it actually comes.

Linda Simpson: At Channel 69 [Pyramid] it was very good because traditionally I would always get the money right from the door.

Bunny: Well, goo goo!

Linda Simpson: No, but I'm just saying that as an example of a good way to get paid.

Bunny: Well, an even better way—when you're working with someone you don't know—is to get paid before you set foot on the stage. If you don't know 'em, you get everything up front.

Linda Simpson: Oh, I see what you're saying. Just as a safety measure.

Bunny: When your reputation is established,

the other, is precisely what makes it an important form. Furthermore, we know that it is important because it rubs us the way it does. Pardon the tautology, but while Spike Lee's *Jungle Fever* is a serviceable reworking of the story of star-crossed lovers, it seems somehow quotidian when compared to the trials of two hard-bitten broads who are divided by race, united by gender; who are actually men and who don't lip-sync their versions of "Love on the Rocks" and "Endless Love." Spike was clearly moving in the right direction, but in a culture already fluent in the language of racial tension, it took a **Sherry Vine** and an **Ebony Jett** (the leading players in the aforementioned *Lesbian Jungle Fever*) to push the idea to the point where it actually made a discernible dent. In a culture fairly obsessed with the notions of beauty and of difference, the rise of the drag queen was, in some twisted fashion, a foregone conclusion. As the boilerplate bugaboos of the past face final absorption into the current zeitgeist, edgier deviants are called for. Enter the drag queen. The fact that most of the greats are coming out of New York was also written in (and by) the stars. After all, if you can work it there . . .

Having endured and prevailed over my own rite of passage as a spectator, I set out, in a less passive mode, to answer some basic questions. Why did drag suddenly seem not only palatable but also, upon occasion, downright hilarious? Why are more and more people feeling the same thing? What is it about New York drag queens that sets them apart from other drag queens? These inquiries, however, turned out to be gravy compared to the larger, more fundamental, more slippery problem of solving the riddle of drag itself. ("I can't define it, but I know it when I see it . . ." just wouldn't suffice.) What is drag? Why is it so powerful? How does it manage to cut so deep into and yet dance so lightly upon our deepest fears and anxieties?

There exists a frustrating variety of notions of precisely what drag is—

you're taking a gamble and they don't realize it. They agree with you and promise you this amount of money, and then if people don't show up or people don't pay, it's their gamble, not yours.

Linda Simpson: Didn't you do that "Country Night" once and it was slow? And then he didn't want to pay you at the end of the night because it was slow?

Bunny: Yes.

Linda Simpson: I mean, that's really crappy.

Bunny: And then he was very surprised. He paid me like half, but then was very surprised when I slammed him later. And he wanted me to work with him again, but I was not gonna.

Linda Simpson: To do the promoting, you gotta take the risk.

Miss Understood: I mean, if someone's your friend and they're going to work with you—

everyone, it turns out, is an expert. Furthermore, terms and appellations differ from locale to locale and from era to era. It would be nice simply to posit that "drag is when a man dresses in women's clothing." The problem is that lots of men do just this (more than most regular folk might like to confess) and yet not all of them are drag queens. Like any complex alchemy, the special mixture of male physiology and female support hose requires a rich and varied lexicon to describe its myriad manifestations. Given the profusion of different types of men who are caught up in the special appeal of swapping swatches, a brief tour of the entire catalog is called for. By separating the wheat from the chaff, we should be able to clarify those crucial qualities that differentiate a man in a dress from a full-fledged drag queen. It is actually easier to back one's way into a working definition of drag per se, so the following, for better or for worse, is a brief catalog of those things that, in New York right now, drag is often mistaken for but, nevertheless, generally is not.

First, you've got your cross-dressers: men who clearly delight in wearing women's clothes, often very stylish ones at that. However, that is where the similarity to drag queens ends. For most cross-dressers, the crossing o'er is essentially the beginning, middle and end of the story. Cross-dressing—a ritual practiced primarlily by straight-identified men—is mostly about the pleasure that accompanies the act alone. These gentlemen derive satisfaction merely from wearing the clothes of the other gender. While they may cross-dress in front of others—often their wives— their behavior has less to do with being the object of spectatorship than does that of drag queens. To cultivate these special needs, clubs and societies proliferate for men whose bliss comes in the form of a current hem line or the classic profile of a Chanel suit. Being strapped in, however, is pretty much where the story ends; the feel of the clothes is often enough. For the drag queen at this point, the juices are only just starting to flow.

maybe work there every week—you want to cut a deal with them, fine. But yeah, it's their responsibility.

Flloyd: You have to know in advance if it's going to be a deal.

Part II: The Future of Drag

Julian: Let me ask you: Is there a different kind of future for drag performers?

Miss Understood: Union!

Julian: Well, that's my question in a sense. Is that a silly thing to hope for?

Flloyd: Interactive drag.

Next, you've got your transvestites, who have plenty in common with cross-dressers, so much so that when you're talking about cross-dressers, it's generally safe to substitute "transvestite." The only salient difference between the two, and tastes will vary, is that the term "transvestite" is often used to describe a man who dresses as a woman in return for some (usually illegal) remuneration. The cross-dresser, arguably possessed of more clinical, domestic inclinations, is generally not.

Furthermore, some men who dress in women's clothes are transsexuals, or at least on their way to becoming so, and that's a horse of a very different, more surgical color. There is occasional overlap between this and the other categories. People who convert biologically have little to do with drag queens in terms of day-to-day life, but inasmuch as the dominant culture has little room for those who exist between the twin poles of male and female, transsexuals, just by getting out of bed in the morning, also represent a significant challenge to the status quo—to say nothing of those who complete only a portion of that transformation. Some drag queens have experimented with more permanent changes; however, they invariably stop short of the surgical point of no return. This is a self-fulfilling prophecy, however, as those queens who, in fact, pass over to the other gender in such a wholesale manner are no longer drag queens and thereby fall outside the scope of any inquiry into what drag queens do. More on this later.

Continuing on, you've got your female impersonators, "gender illusionists" as they sometimes refer to themselves, but their objectives are likewise not perfectly consonant with those of the New York drag queen. Most of the men who fall under this heading are professionals who are paid to recreate, in as uncanny a way as possible (that is to say, with little irony or critical distance), the personae of genuinely legendary genuine women. The only hitch is that the women most frequently chosen for impersonation

Bunny: Maybe you're joking, but everyone could be helped by a union. I don't understand, if there's such a big drag craze now, why someone hasn't come along with organizational skills and said, "I can make money off of these bitches and have great, great contacts."

Hapi Phace: Well, maybe not a union, maybe an agency to begin with. We don't even have that.

Miss Understood: Well, I have one.

Hapi Phace: Yeah, but—

Flloyd: As long as Hedda Lettuce will do it for free, how can any of us get paid properly?

Miss Understood: But see, no. Club work is by nature so illegal. You couldn't have a union because so much of it's off the books anyway and it's not really all done, like, officially, so—

Bunny: But you'd have to have a lot more to work with . . .

could practically be considered drag queens themselves. In the female impersonator's stable one typically finds Marilyn Monroe, Barbra Streisand, Bette Midler, Bette Davis, Tina Turner, Judy Garland and daughter Liza, Joan Crawford and Cher, to name a few. To the extent that these women are already avatars of beauty, heaping bowls full of glamour and fame, for a drag queen to impersonate them would be, very simply, redundant. Furthermore, the drag queens of New York prefer to create their own characters rather than try to embody ones that have already been done—and done better. The act of female impersonation is just that: impersonation. Drag in New York cares little for uncanny recreations of female icons; it has a distance from its own creations that female impersonation, by definition, cannot have.

There is no dearth of other, more grandiose misconceptions about drag; sentiments which go beyond mere confusion about which terms to apply. From outside the relative safety of clubs and community come all sorts of fire-and-brimstone mongers, demagogues and nut cases who rail endlessly about the wickedness of drag. The bizarre fellowship between the fundamentalist Christian Right and factions of the feminist left that emerged around the issue of pornography, for example, now also includes the drag queen on its list of postmodern boogeymen. Working in the service of understandably different agendas, these otherwise polarized groups have found a common purpose in decrying the evils of men who wear women's clothes. The Right revels in Dante-esque images of (family) value-less sexual deviants out to recruit and corrupt an otherwise God-fearing nation, while certain censurious feminist voices argue that when a man dresses in drag he is engaging in the gender equivalent of wearing blackface. If, as they contend, the various items that drag queens affect (wigs, heels, makeup, etc.) comprise the uniform of an enslaved underclass, then for a man to put them on in a mocking way is to add an insufferable insult

---

Miss Understood: Stricter standards than just, you know—

Bunny: . . . when they say, "I want a crazy art scene actor, I want a traditional Diana Ross lip-sync."

Miss Understood: You know what the problem is? Their standards just go down. Everyone keeps telling me that before I was working, that in like '87, you got paid a lot more in the clubs. Now I work in these places where they think, "Why should I pay you a hundred and fifty if I can pay fifty or seventy-five to some kid with big stacky shoes from Brooklyn that just came out last week?" *That* looks like shit, but they figure, "Well, it's freaky enough, it'll impress them enough and whatever." I mean, that's just it. There's always new people and they're always willing to—

Bunny: That's what's *bad*!

Miss Understood: —they're always willing to

to an already unjustifiable injury. That a double-barreled collusion as diabolical as this developed at all means that the offering up of the drag queen as the latest national boil to be lanced must be a source of considerable political mileage. Any bed large enough to sleep lovers like these is worth at least a second look. On the other hand, it would be unfair and disingenuous to suggest that either religious leaders or feminists think monolithically. In the same way that no one drag queen represents the attitudes of the entire so-called drag queen community, it is wasteful to presume that there is a feminist "position" about drag. There is not. In fact, some of the most exciting and mature theories about the nature of drag and other similar forms of gender subversion has come from non-reactionary feminist writers and critics.

From less vitriolic quarters comes the most universal reaction. "Pathetic" is the word often used by the tolerant uninitiated to describe the poor soul who drifts wanly from unfulfilled female yearning to unfulfilled female yearning, hopelessly stretching diminutive, if well-coordinated gabardine ensembles over the tortured frame of his male physique. One can't be certain where this widespread notion first gained a foothold, especially when one considers cultures and eras other than our own in which queens enjoyed quite a different embrace from the world at large. Most likely, such ideas are the product of a macho blah-blah culture which loathes nothing quite so much as a feminized man. But perhaps something else is at work; perhaps it is true that these folks just aren't getting the joke.

So what is the joke? If these are all the things that drag is not, then what is it? For my money, the quality that redeems it from all of the above dull misconceptions and admonishments is its theatricality. By this, I don't mean that a night at the Pyramid equals a Night of the Iguana, only that good drag done well does to the human body what good drama does to the human condition:

lower their standards for people that aren't really turning out as well, but they don't care.

Flloyd: Because Hedda will do it for free.

Bunny: I think clubs did used to pay more.

Flloyd: I used to get a thousand dollars for the parties at Tunnel, when Rudolph was running it.

Miss Understood: You did not!

Flloyd: I did too.

Hapi Phace: I used to get a thousand for the Michael Todd room, five hundred or a thousand for a show.

Miss Understood: But how many people would that be?

Bunny: A thousand for dancing at Danceteria—

Hapi Phace: Well, one person would get five hundred to a thousand. I mean, it depended—five hundred was the low rate. Maybe a big part of it

it heightens and enlarges it for the purpose of getting a better look. By stretching hyper-idealized versions of the female anatomy almost to the breaking point, drag insists that we question the worth of those very ideals. It's not about mocking the female body or its accouterments, but about ballooning those aspects to the point where their absurdity is laid bare. In other words, even if the queen is not standing on a stage, drag is theater of the ridiculous taken to its most existentially ridiculous.

Dollar for dollar, some of the best theater in town is being practiced by queens—the key to whose success is the extent to which they refuse to take themselves, and the pulchritude they parody, too seriously. Rare is the queen who actually wants to be a woman. On the contrary, the essence of drag for those who do it is irony. And any reader of, say, Harold Bloom will know that irony is among the highest of the arts. What drag queens bring to their work that is missing from that of others who trade in sartorial subterfuge is a critical distance from the characters they create. This is why many of the women who are impersonated by female impersonators are already more like drag queens than are the impersonators themselves. For example, inasmuch as a performer like Cher presents, while in performance, really the *idea* of Cher—a theatrical representation of glamour, fame and hyper-idealized femininity called "Cher"—she displays all of the characteristics of drag. The distance at which Cher the woman stands from "Cher" the character may not be as great as that which exists between the garden-variety drag performer and his drag persona, but nevertheless, the distance is there. To impersonate Cher on stage, in other words, may be an act of gender illusion, but to *be* Cher on stage is, for all practical purposes, to be a drag queen.

What all of this irony succeeds in doing, then, aside from providing a few good laughs, is critiquing putative societal notions of what the feminine and the masculiune are supposed to be like. Through parody and theatrics,

was—well, I don't want to put any blame on anyone—but it seems like when people like Suzanne [Bartsch] came along, who would do a whole night and bring all these people in, and then she'd tell these queens who she knew were broke, "I'll pay you fifty dollars. You just stand on a box. You don't have to do a show." It became a thing of just becoming a freak on a box rather than being a performer.

Bunny: Even when she puts on a show, Suzanne'll

do it laboriously slow, far too long. But I think that's part of the trend of mega, pumping discos, especially the gay discos, where—unlike the Pyramid, where we were spoiled—people do not stop the dance music and pay attention to a twenty-minute floor show. They just don't. They won't. Or like Channel 69, which had a more funky, mixed, intelligent crowd—very different from its hostess—that enjoyed dancing and cruising, but *also* enjoyed watching a show that had some meat to it, and not

sexual mimicry and innuendo, the drag queen presents, by his/her very existence, a caricature not only of femininity but also of his own masculinity as it is understood by mainstream, commercial culture—with an emphasis on the commercial. By donning a pair of false breasts, eyelashes and the sine qua non of drag, a wig, drag automatically asks the question: what is it we expect of our women and our men? By exaggerating most, if not all, of the female anatomy and traditional modes of dress, the drag queen highlights the unnaturalness of the expectations that we have for these body parts and the items in which they come wrapped. To quote another queen whose drag extends beyond gender to encompass the very act of living itself, "It's a good thing."

And there's more! (Oh yes, drag is the gift that keeps on giving.) Right next to irony on the list of cultural/textual constructs melting under the hot gaze of the eager drag queen is glamour. Irony without glamour is dull and unsexy, while glamour without irony is the Rose Bowl Parade. Put them together, however, and let the games begin. Drag is fairly obsessed with the notion of glamour and those for whom glamour is a central, guiding principle. Whether she's working the image of the supermodel, the movie queen, the royal family member, the rock star or the good girl gone so bad that she's made it to the cover of at least several tabloids, rare is the drag queen who is not in some fundamental fashion exhibiting a sense of glamour. Of course, glamour is nothing more than the outward, primarily sartorial expression of wealth and once again we're back to square one: what a commercial, consumer society wants of its ideal woman. Take the perfect set of breasts, a great pair of legs, terrific bones and a lot of cash, mix well and presto! glamour arrives. What the drag queen knows implicitly is that few women (and fewer men) can reasonably live up to that ideal. Drag itself gains a great deal of power from the distance it creates between the disdain it has for commercial-

just a track act with two dancers, which is the only kind of thing that—like, Roxy doesn't even have shows.

Flloyd: A lot of the big clubs have phased out entertainment, period.

Bunny: Totally. 'Cause the emphasis is on boys, and on go-go boys, and muscle men. That's what's on the invites, that's what's on the tickets.

Flloyd: I tried to get Michael Alig to let me do a cabaret in the basement of the Tunnel, but they don't want entertainment.

Hapi Phace: The thing is, they get enough people coming in there to see guys in their underwear. You know, how much does *that* outfit cost them? So they can pay them fifty.

Flloyd: And *they* get tipped.

Hapi Phace: Right. They get tipped. And the thing is, fifty dollars is like cab fare and half a wig or

ized standards of beauty and its uncanny ability to bring those very ideals to life—sort of.

When one watches a drag queen at work, it is strange how rarely one has the sensation that one is watching a woman. Those spectators of New York drag who come in the hopes of viewing/experiencing the uncanny, therefore, are in for a disappointment; the fantasy locked within drag is one of mixed emotions, not of absolutes. For those who expect the ironic, the parodic and the satiric, however, there is much to enjoy. For those who maintain that drag is inherently misogynistic, well, only a few minutes in the presence of **The Misstress Formika** prove that argument as valid as one that maintains that Bozo is a misanthrope. To view drag as hateful or even mocking of women is to miss the irony that is at its heart.

To anyone who considers themselves both a feminist and "pro-drag," the issue has little to do with a queen's trying to be "like a woman"—be the effort well-intentioned or otherwise—and everything to do with his trying *not* to be "like a man." From this perspective, drag is essentially an act of liberation, a push to shake the yoke of masculine expectations attached to the accident of being male. Surely the heart of even the most militant feminist has room in it for those men who feel as shackled by macho ideals as any woman might be by feminine ones. That in shedding those masculine qualities, the queen chooses not to dress as, say, an ostrich or for that matter a doorknob, is surely due to the fact that the natural antidote to the masculine, especially in a culture so averse to anything in between, is the feminine. The wigs, corsets and heels that once tortured those who were forced to wear them are, in this scenario, swept up and transformed by the radical gesture—of a man who dons them willingly. Any objection to that gesture or effort to fetishize those objects as sacred in their profanity seems almost reactionary.

hose. Something, though, that's really different about back then when we got paid all that money: today, you get dressed at home, you take a cab, you go to the club, you show up, you get paid (hopefully) and you take a cab home. But back when—in the old days, when the Ancient Ones were working—you went to the Pyramid or a smaller club, they had a lot of performers. And you had dressing rooms. They actually provided a dressing room. Like a lot of these places don't even. And you *hung out* and you saw your friends, you saw all the queens, you hung out with the queens backstage, you know, and that was a big *communal* part of it. And some of the clubs, like the Pyramid, were run by queens. So they knew how to treat us. But now, we're working for these people—we're freaks to them.

Bunny: And we had lighting men, and sound men. That spoiled me more than anything, 'cause these million-dollar clubs cannot even get a goddamn cassette to run. The tape stops mid-number! A light

Those who would argue that drag queens are merely men who wish they were women fail to grasp that the power of drag grows directly out of the effect of layering one gender on top of the other. In drag, one gender cannot make do without the other. To watch a drag queen at work and think "how sad" is to miss the point. For if the assumption is that the drag queen is just a self-loathing malcontent acting out a deep-rooted fantasy of gender transformation, then the idea of drag is effectively canceled out. For when a man who wishes to be woman (or vice-versa) finally succeeds in becoming one, then he is no longer a drag queen. Surgery has replaced theater in that scenario and that's no fun. The special, theatrical power of mixing the two genders is lost. The Drag Queens of New York are particularly vehement on this issue and can be counted on to express their enthusiasm for their own maleness whether in or out of a wig.

Furthermore, in this interpretation, the archness and bitchiness that get layered on top of the actual cross-dressing and which are themselves so often the target of "feminist" ire, likewise have little to do with women. That added campiness is an expression of gay identity specifically. It is a kind of age-old code used by a hidden population both to identify itself and to express the bitterness that comes from generations of repression and institutional anxiety. Does anyone imagine that if gay life had never been forced to exist underground there would ever have been a thing called camp? Readers of drag must always bear in mind that simply because a man is parading around in an old Edith Head knockoff shouting lines from *Mommie Dearest* that he is not necessarily espousing that look or that behavior. Perhaps it is a knee-jerk political reaction or merely a widespread failure of readership that causes so many to assume that everything a person enjoys or creates or represents artistically is necessarily being promoted by him or her. Drag is not a religion and queens don't proselytize. If

that never once touches the hostess—of course, Linda was hosting so maybe I can understand that—but I mean, it is ridiculous. It really is. They're not geared towards performance. And if a club is big enough, it's not going to be populated by mainly funky, intelligent people. It's going to be—well, but they pay my salary, so you know—

Julian: So what's going on, then?

Bunny: It's the Death of Downtown!

Miss Understood: It's quantity over quality.

Hapi Phace: Exactly.

Linda Simpson: You mean how drag is supposedly so big, and yet there's so few drag venues that are decent?

Flloyd: There's nowhere where I can do a weird twenty-minute show.

Julian: Well, you did that one at Pyramid—

anything, they see the versions of femininity they create as the grotesque reflection of their own sense of shame and difference, and the farthest thing from what they know women (and by extension, themselves) to be. Rare is the queen who, despite her own pleasure at squeezing her spare tire into a death-defying corset, would recommend that anyone—man or woman—follow suit.

Perhaps most interesting though is this: after interviewing literally dozens upon dozens of drag queens, all of whom are basically bored to death with talking about what they do and why they do it, it became apparent to me that hardly any of them ever talk about gender. Ever! Unless they are specifically coaxed to address it, gender and its ancillary political issues are for them perhaps the least interesting aspect of their work. Certainly, they are as ready to talk about gender as anyone, if that's what people want to discuss, but their gaze is generally fixed on other more immediate concerns. The sorts of bitchy remarks they seem addicted to making at the expense of one another's bodies clearly have less to do with hatred or mistrust of the female body than the fulfillment of an age-old gay tradition of acidic banter and tongue-in-cheek rivalry. The campiness and exaggerated "feminine" characteristics so prevalent in drag have much more to do with acting out gay stereotypes than female ones.

This may be the crucial distinction separating those who do drag from those who just talk about it. In the same way that generations have held to the ridiculous notion that homosexuality is merely a neurotic byproduct of a fear of heterosexual intercourse, observers of drag have tended to assume that drag is a queen's way of acting out his disgust with the alien female body—the same fear and disgust that "made him gay" in the first place. For the majority of queens themselves, drag is no more a reaction to women or the female body than summer is a reaction to fall. Gender is the

Chicklet: That was at eight o'clock at night . . . and ten people came.

Hapi Phace: Things are just changing. I mean, that's just part of the change. It's like what happens with everything. It changes. The situation has changed.

Bunny: The Pyramid and the Boy Bar were really communal-type places where there was a guru, and he—

Flloyd: They were more like theater.

Bunny: Yeah. I really miss the Boy Bar having their shows. That was a real tragedy when it closed.

Julian: Now that Pyramid and Boy Bar are closed to drag, who's going to pick up that slack?

Miss Understood: Me!

Hapi Phace: Not us! We never ran those clubs. We might have had our own night, but we did not run those clubs.

Miss Understood: The Pyramid went down

code most effectively broken down to create a sense of drama, style and camp. It is the quickest route to the fabulousness that is the true heart of drag.

Perhaps the essence of drag—from a queen's perspective—was best summed up by **Holly Woodlawn,** the one surviving member of Andy Warhol's famous troika of drag superstars, as she is quoted in Martin Duberman's *Stonewall:* "It's not a man or a woman, it's fabulous. When men's fashions start to be more fabulous, I'll use *them* to dress up." While few queens have offered explanations as concise and unassailable, hours of conversation reveal a similar sentiment throughout the drag community. Of course gender is a part of what queens do and think about, and surely there are those whose wretched feelings about the female body are played out in their drag, but for the most part, queens are far more interested in simply heightening their sense of self, looking amazing and getting away with antics that in shirtsleeves would get them hauled off to the nut house.

There is no avoiding the fact that drag is kind of weird. Even for those who enjoy it, from both sides of the mascara, there is a strangeness that cannot be denied. The challenge is to see past that threatening quality and into the harmless heart of the thing. Coming to terms with drag, for those who give a darn, is a lot like coming to terms with one's own nightmares. The journey may be hellish, but the rewards are likely to be worth it. And oddly enough, drag, especially in New York, for all its strangeness, has undergone a fundamental change: it has succeeded. Queens have always borne the burden of an overriding desire to cross over, so to speak. In their obsession with iconography they are fairly lit up with their own ambition to become something bigger than what they are. Even in a pre-**RuPaul** culture, drag always pined most for those figures who possess money, style, fame and beauty. The joke was that so much of what the

when the ownership changed, because by the time *I* got to the Pyramid, we had no money. The club gave us no money. We had what we pulled in at the door to put on a show. You know, a good club will make money at the bar and will say, "Fine. We'll pay for advertising to get people in here. We'll give you some of the money. We'll give you a budget." It didn't work that way by the time I got there. The owners who had it at that point said it's like renting out a space and they make the money off the bar.

Flloyd: And *you* had to replace the microphone if it broke, and *you* had to buy new lightbulbs.

Hapi Phace: This was not how it *was*, you know, but these clubs got cheaper and cheaper toward the performers because they *thought* we were making all this money.

Julian: There was a time at the Pyramid when there was a lot of money being made, right?

drag queen did was a reaction to her own distance from that which she emulated. She was always acutely aware that practically speaking she could embody that glamour only in an ironic way; she could never actually achieve the sort of crossover appeal that is the purview of genuine female icons—until now.

The arrival of recording artist and international drag superstar **RuPaul** represents the realization of what was once only a fantasy: the widespread commodification of an actual drag queen. The strange conundrum that this presents then is this: if so much of the energy of drag is generated by its outsider status, what will fuel it if it finds acceptance, even absorption, into the mainstream? In other words, if the neurotic fantasy of a cross-dressed, cross-over success is realized, then what will that subversive form subvert next? The answer, in all likelihood, will be drag itself. As is probably inevitable as we hurdle willy-nilly toward the new millennium, drag is becoming increasingly self-conscious and self-referential. Whereas most of what drag used to reflect was everything that happened outside of the hermetic seal of gay life, as that seal begins to deteriorate, much of what contemporary drag will address is drag itself. What, say, the cubists were to the lyric representational artists of the nineteenth century, contemporary New York drag queens are to the high drag goddesses of yesteryear. Really.

Finally, queens have gotten smart. The entertainment industry's voracious appetite for anything that can keep consumers consuming means that today's media-savvy downtown dominatrix can be tomorrow's supermodel of the world—if she plays her cards right. Since the current architects of fashion, music and style rely so heavily on club and street life for their inspiration (and by extension, for their manses in Montauk), it was only a matter of time before the auto-luminescent denizens of the deep got sucked up into the machinery and spat back out on a global scale. **RuPaul** is only

Bunny: Oh, hand over fist.

Hapi Phace: There was a time at the Pyramid where if we didn't make it at the door, the club owners would make it up to the performers out of the bar. It's changed to this point where if we don't make it at the door, someone doesn't get paid, you know? Or you get paid less. And you can't do that to queens very long. You can only do that to a queen once or twice before she's says, "I'm not performing there anymore."

Julian: Only once or twice?

Miss Understood: I mean, with most queens it could only happen to them once and they're going to say, "I'm not going to perform there anymore." I mean, why would you? Why would anyone go? If you went to a restaurant and you ordered a meal for twenty dollars, and the bill comes and they say, "Oh, it's forty. We have to pay the dishwasher," you're not going to go back there to eat! It's the same thing with a queen. She spent fifty dollars on

the beginning. Like a school of great whites rabidly following the scent of bloody chum, the Drag Queens of New York are hot on the trail of widespread popular appeal. The skills they honed while preening for the dim pop of the occasional instamatic flashbulb through the smoked-filled haze of cramped cabarets are about to pay off. The glare of the klieg lights is oh so much brighter, but few understand how to find their hot spots like these seasoned showstoppers. Fame costs and they've been paying their dues for quite a while. The new generation of New York drag queens has tossed aside the dismal bathos of their pioneering forebears. No longer stigmatized by old world attitudes about gender and good PR, they've set their phasers for stun and anything is possible.

For the student of this phenomenon, the challenge is that what one imagined was but a narrow slice of urban subculture is actually a vast, far-reaching movement which sneaks around corners and peeks through the curtains on a surprising number of levels of municipal life. The subject, once addressed, unfurls endlessly in front of the increasingly vertiginous viewer. An inquiry that looked as if it would require considerable padding turns out to be a big bolt of thickly woven fabric that needs substantial cutting to make bearable. Welcome to the zany, brainy world of the Drag Queens of New York.

---

her look and she's getting paid a hundred, and then you say, "All we made was enough to pay you fifty." She didn't make any money. She's not coming back there. I mean, we're not fools.

Julian: So then what you're saying is there's no hope?

Miss Understood: I think different venues will eventually pop up. It's just that they go through phases.

Flloyd: Even those big clubs that are making fifty thousand dollars a night will try to dick you over on the money.

Bunny: Yeah, yeah, yeah. But I was saying to Linda the other night, at Palladium—at their big pumping gay night—we were sitting at the bar, watching Candis spin around wildly, and I was saying, "We're supposed to be performers!" I mean, we're just . . .

Linda Simpson: "Impotent" was the word you used.

The Drag Queens of New York: A Rather Brief History

The story of drag in New York is a tough one to tell. Like all good mysteries, it reveals itself in its own time and then only when its characters are ready. While certain names, dates and even brief stretches of history are accessible through conventional means—the card catalog, the occasional scholarly work, the obituaries—the vast majority of evidence regarding the Drag Queens of New York lies with them, wherever they are. The merciless vicissitudes of our particular era have exacted a steep toll on those queens who should be here, gracefully growing older, dispensing their knowledge or writing books of their own. The combination of tough times, hard living and unyielding nature has ravaged no population more than

Bunny: Yeah, I mean we're not being used the way we ought to be used. We're just sitting there, as decoration.

Linda Simpson: I said, "drag welfare."

Bunny: Exactly! It's so easy, and it is lucrative, so you can't really turn it down. To walk into a club and get handed a stack of drink tickets and priss around all night while other people are paying to do just that. It's just so—it's easy!

Linda Simpson: But at the same time it *is* like drag welfare. It kind of keeps you, like, you know . . .[Slumps in her chair.]

Bunny: Well, that's your own laziness.

Linda Simpson: Well, maybe it is. You know what I mean?

Julian: [To Linda.] Why did you stop doing your stuff at Pyramid?

Bunny: Everybody hated it.

that which witnessed and nurtured the great flowering of drag in New York that began in the early sixties and which even now seems yet to reach the height of its tumescence.

If we are now in the midst of a golden age of drag, then it is a flower whose seed has been incubating literally for centuries. Regardless of the history of theatrical cross-dressing, or the many ancient cultures, including Native American, in which crossing gender lines was ritualized or otherwise indemnified by custom, the history of good ol' down and dirty drag queen–style drag in New York City is old and rich. It is worth differentiating between the former types of drag and the kind that is the focus of this guide. The queens examined herein—and their many flowery forebears—have been functioning (at best) in spite of and (at worst) in direct violation of prevailing societal mores and codes of conduct. In the legit theater, the suspension of disbelief that is at the heart of the dramatic experience excuses all sorts of behavior that, were it to occur outside of the protective embrace of the theater itself, would engender no end of outrage and punishment. In other words, pure drag has a distinct outlaw quality.

New York has long proven an irresistible magnet for all manner of men who dress like women, or, more correctly, in women's clothes. In 1741, New York's Hyde Park was named after Edward Hyde, governor of the then royal provinces of New York and New Jersey from 1702 to 1708. Hyde was a notorious cross-dresser whose reputed devotion to his beloved Queen Anne, so he said, compelled him to emulate her in every fashion available to him. The truth of his justification notwithstanding, his behavior was viewed with the utmost disdain by his colleagues and peers, who, expressing a sentiment that continues to be echoed today, found his drag to be a pathetic reflection of the moral lassitude of the society as a whole. His decolletage was seen as a symbol of a general turpitude which had infected the municipal system and would surely destroy the city as a whole were it not confronted and

Linda Simpson: We had it for two and a half years!

Miss Understood: The Board of Health closed her down.

Linda Simpson: No, we'd done it for two and a half years. The signs were there that it was fading a teensy bit.

Miss Understood: I hope not.

Chicklet: *I* certainly think so.

Julian: Maybe now one of the few places where a drag "artist"—someone who thinks conceptually—can put together a show—over which she has control and in which she can present things as she sees them—is on cable TV.

Flloyd: It doesn't pay. *You* have to pay.

Bunny: *You* have to *pay* to do it. That's my problem with it.

Flloyd: And the rewards are not immediate.

removed. Hyde was eventually ousted from his position and died in debtors' prison, cursed as the living embodiment of his cursed affliction.

The history of New York's love affair with the drag queen since then (so long and so strong is that relationship that love somehow feels like the right word) is the story of just a small stretch of land that, while it has changed names from time to time, has never changed its essential role as home to nature and society's many merry misfits. Start at either of the two mighty rivers that churn along the shoals of ol' Manhattan's mythic shores—either the Hudson to the west, or the East to the, well, east—just where they are intersected by Fourteenth Street, the northern border of Downtown. Queens have been strolling this street's sunny sidewalks and patronizing its dingy discount dime stores for centuries. Some twenty blocks below the Realto, as Fourteenth Street has also been known, Canal Street represents the southern border of the region. Most of the nineteenth century's drag dramas were played out between these two streets, many of them to the east, on the Bowery. A broad stretch of thoroughfare that from the air looks like the southern tail of Third Avenue, the Bowery is described thus by Luc Sante in his history *Low Life*:

> Until fairly recently, the Bowery has always possessed the greatest number of groggeries, flophouses, clip joints, brothels, fire sales, rigged auctions, pawnbrokers, dime museums, shooting galleries, dime-a-dance establishments, fortune telling salons, lottery agencies, thieves' markets and tattoo parlors, as well as theaters of the second, third, fifth and tenth rank. It is also a fact that the Bowery is the only major thoroughfare in New York never to have a single church built on it.

An entire century of drag can be understood in terms of the ebb and flow of gay life on the Bowery and around Greenwich Village. Cycles of rel-

Miss Understood: And not that many people see it.

Bunny: I don't have cable. I don't know. But just from what I get of it from other people, there are very, very, very few shows, if any—and this is from people who sit and flip around cable, like Lahoma, all the time—shows that they *plan* to watch on cable. Even if it's one of their favorites. Lahoma likes *Brandy and Brenda,* but she doesn't really sit down and make an effort to watch it.

Hapi Phace: She doesn't schedule it.

Bunny: Yeah. And I know very few people who do.

Chicklet: Well, I don't know who's gonna sit and plan their schedule around a cable show, but it *is* another venue. Because if you're someone who lives on 110th Street and you don't go down to Boy Bar or whatever, it is an opportunity to see what's going on down there or who's running about. Something like *The Hedda Lettuce Show,* where she actually has people come on and do

ative openness are followed by waves of moralism and civil vigilance during which houses of ill repute are raided, throngs of fairies, pansies, girlie-boys, queens, queers and faggots (as they have betimes been known) are tossed into jail and a new set of sumptuary laws are enacted designed to limit the dress, conduct and status of men deemed a threat to the very fabric of society as a whole. Notorious houses of ill repute, saloons like the Slide, were home to all manner of cross-dressing tomfoolery. Paresis and Webster halls (the latter still a favorite haunt of drag queens and other stalwarts) were, over the years, home to fantastic drag balls and masquerades. In an era in which cross-dressing was forbidden by law and viewed as a sure sign of depravity, transgressors of those codes were helpless to defend themselves against interdiction of any kind, be it by the police or roving bands of angry kids.

This dynamic remained in place well into the middle of the twentieth century, a time during which New York was viewed increasingly as the center of the Western world. Even as the "pansies"—the nineteenth century equivalent of latter day "street queens"—of the Bowery were enduring the periodic harassment at the hands of forces both private and municipal, female impersonater Julian Eltinge was becoming one of vaudeville's biggest stars. Widely regarded as the greatest drag performer of his day—he was not thought of as gay—he commanded the second largest salary in vaudeville history and even had a Forty-second Street theater named for him.

The twenties and thirties were again a time of relative openness, a fact that was true for all New Yorkers. As Europe struggled to recover from the ravages of World War I, America remained remarkably unscathed. It was the Jazz Era, a time of unprecedented creative exuberance for America. Virtually all of the writers, poets, musicians, composers, artists and critics who comprised the bulk of the U.S. creative vanguard at the time were

numbers, it's another venue to perform in that sense. Or if you're producing your own show, like I do, you know? That's actually a half hour a week that I'm just pushing myself out there and whoever catches it catches it. It's not going to replace live work, but—

Flloyd: But you might go in the hole! You don't get paid for that. So as far as a medium that drag queens are going to seek out, I don't know if it's—

Chicklet: But something on public access costs nothing. What does it cost me? The tape and cab fare if I have to go somewhere.

Flloyd: Well, production costs.

Chicklet: On Channel 35 they have commercials or sponsors or whatever.

Bunny: See, that's why I think. I have never seen your show and I don't have cable, and I'm not slamming the medium. Cable TV can be great.

packed together on the tiny island of Manhattan. It was an age when effeminacy in men could be excused as a kind of highbrow foppery, when the brutish machismo that built the country and fought its early wars seemed obsolete. New Yorkers were reaping the fruits of prosperity and longevity, and gay life, even though it remained largely underground, flourished.

The early twentieth century also marked the rise of New York as the center of American bohemian life, a café society whose epicenter was Greenwich Village. Artists and intellectuals gathered to trade ideas and debate the merits of various philosophies and political systems as well as the nature of mankind, art and sexuality. Experimentation was the order of the day, as the Village, with its speakeasies, communist bookstores and cabarets became a sort of open-air shopping mall for sexually curious, transgressive tourists and wealthy dilettantes looking for a cozy place to slum. Little has changed.

The Depression and World War II, neither of which Americans could avoid, all but destroyed the world of New York drag. As always, of course, an underground remained active, but the strain that bankruptcy and then war put on American manliness forced more gay and transgendered people than ever to keep their differences to themselves. Octogenarian drag star **Minette,** who began performing as a child, recalls that during a raid on the Black Cat, a Greenwich Village speakeasy, in which he was doing an impression of Belle Baker, a Sophie Tucker–style vaudeville performer, "they hid me in a garbage can then said I was a midget!" The war years forever changed the way Americans dealt with manhood; queenliness would no longer be embraced. Effeminacy was once again viewed as a sign of weakness. During the militarization not only of the economy, but also of the culture as a whole, such displays were frowned upon.

The euphoria that accompanied the end of the war saw a slow reemergence of drag—if only within New York's cultural landscape. The return of the boys to native soil meant business would be brisk in New York's sex

But the fact that you do have to *pay* is what has kept . . . I mean, Linda and I have discussed it time and time again, about trying to do a show. My problem with cable shows is that they're difficult to watch because they lack production value. Which is one thing that I thought was very unusual about [Dolores] [*The Pot*]. He would have little segments with a graphic on there that would indicate the beginning of a new segment. And that is very rare. Most of it's just like chop, chop, chop, chop. And almost always very long. Way too long of a segment, because they're trying to fill up half an hour. It's hard work.

Chicklet: That depends on the individual show, producer, or whatever. But you could take something like *The Mrs. Mouth Show*—which I do consider a drag show because it's a guy's chin dressed as a woman—and that costs nothing. That costs nothing, and I think it's one of the funniest things on television.

Bunny: It is. It really is.

industries, which offered everything from cross-dressers, to showgirls, to prostitutes and various combinations of these. Seeing the opportunity that arose with the Allied victory in 1945, club owner and impresario Pat Patillo opened a string of downtown clubs that would feature drag and which would come to represent the pinnacle of many a queen's career for more than thirty years.

Hanging his first shingle on the corner of Third Street and Sixth Avenue in late 1945, Patillo opened the Howdy, a nightclub that featured an entirely cross-dressed revue.

Fran Lebowitz
Author

These are not real lives in the ordinary sense. They're in a movie, and their whole life is that way. That is something that I think a lot of people who don't know drag queens don't understand. Even the ones that are kind of funny and witty—Candy [Darling] was, kind of, Jackie [Curtis] was, certainly—there's no real sense of irony here. There is something intrinsically earnest about being a drag queen. There is something earnest at the level of a child. The tone is camp. It's taken from things that are meant to be ironic, but it is not really ironic. It is really earnest. To me, it's earnest in the most profound way, which is why, at the bottom level, at base, it's not interesting to me. It's blatant. You could not say that being a drag queen is a subtle pursuit. It's a very blatant thing and it's very childish. . . . Of course they don't [have any sense of irony]. This is their life! You're watching it, but this is their life.

It was just the sort of lowbrow sensation that attracted hordes of decommissioned military men looking for that special someone to welcome them home and help pass the time. The first club of its kind, really, its reputation spread rapidly, fueled by the military network's word of mouth. Sensing a trend and looking to upgrade, Patillo soon moved his operation uptown a bit, where he opened the first of his two clubs named after their addresses.

In 1950, at 181 Second Avenue he opened the 181 Club, which, much like the Howdy, featured drag performers and live musicians. Patillo was adamant, however, about appealing to a diverse audience. He had no inter-

Chicklet: So I think it's the individual show. It is another valid option for people.

Bunny: Yeah, it is, but we were just saying—

Miss Understood: There's only so big it can get because it is cable. And the problem with it—

Julian: It can get syndicated. [Dolores] keeps hinting—

Miss Understood: Yeah, everyone keeps hoping that. I just don't have that much hope.

Bunny: I think that for the energy that you have to put into it to make something that I would consider watchable—and like I say, I don't have cable so I don't know any of them—there might be other ways to expend your energy that would create more publicity or more, you know, desire to see you or . . . whatever.

Flloyd: We need another live venue.

Julian: What about *Jackie 60*?

est in running an exclusively "gay" establishment. He would insist that the "girls" wear men's clothing upon entering and leaving the club. He struggled to attract as many straight patrons as he could by appealing to the theatrical aspect of the revue. The club was, after all, only a few doors away from the Second Avenue Theater, today a cinema, which was at the time a legitimate off-Broadway house and for years the flagship of New York's Yiddish theater community.

The 181 Club was small, however, and it would be a matter of only three years before Patillo moved again, this time to a space near the corner of Second Avenue and East Fourth Street. Opening in 1953, the 82 Club would remain a hot spot of drag activity in New York almost until 1980. It was considered the best job in town for the serious drag performer. A female veteran of the club who goes only by the name Tommy was hired, "butch lesbian that I was," as a waiter; gender play was apparently worked into every aspect of the 82 Club experience. "All the performers had to be twenty-one," recalls Tommy, who, when the club closed in 1978, walked next door to La Mama, New York's leading avant-garde theatrical complex, and was given a job as a stage manager she's never left. She also recalls that, despite the strict dress codes and age requirements at the 82 Club, when the preternaturally beautiful and underage **International Chrysis** applied for work there, someone conveniently forgot to ask her age.

By the mid-sixties the 82 Club had become a legitimate tourist attraction, often drawing celebrities and socialites who were no longer afraid to be seen slumming it a little. Tommy recalls one night when, dressed in her uniform of slacks, jacket and bow tie, she waited a table that included among others Liz Taylor, Eddie Fisher and Tyrone Power. Dinah Washington and Laurence Harvey were two other stars she recalls serving, but that might have been a different night. No matter, the 82 Club, which has

Miss Understood: That's one.

Bunny: *Jackie 20.*

Linda Simpson: *Jackie 20?*

Bunny: That's all you get paid. [Laughter.]

Flloyd: I have to say, *Jackie 60* is the only place I've ever worked where they have paid me *more* than they told me they were going to pay me. Consistently.

Bunny: And like a jerk you pointed out the mistake and gave it back to 'em.

Miss Understood: Everybody I've talked to has actually liked working there.

Flloyd: If they do really well, they'll pay you more than they promised you—well, some people.

Bunny: That's right. And it really has kind of a Pyramid-like feeling. One of my favorite things

since served as a lesbian bar, and rock-and-roll club and triple-x theater, attracted the widest range of patrons, both highbrow and otherwise. The club featured three shows a night, starting at around ten, which included solo singers, live music and large ensemble numbers worthy of any supper club.

Concurrent with the rise of the 82 Club was the ascendance of the older Jewel Box Review, where the aforementioned **Minette** was a member and which toured the whole eastern seaboard, taking drag to odd little clubs in unlikely little cities such as Harrisburg and Buffalo. Known for its interracial acts and emphasis on drag kings as well as queens, the Jewel Box was to drag what Ringling Brothers is to clowns: difficult, dangerous but consistent work. According to Tommy of the 82 Club, the Jewel Box was considered by her girls as a sort of training ground for up-and-comers. Girls developed their chops on the road with the Jewel Box and then—maybe—they were given a shot at the big time at "the 82."

Both the Jewel Box Review and the 82 Club prospered well into the next couple of decades, even as the cultural, political and sexual landscapes began to shift violently around them. The sixties were, of course, a time of seismic change in virtually every aspect of American life. Nothing seemed certain and anything seemed possible, good and bad. For drag, they were years of explosive growth and self-awareness, a time when queens and drag performers (distinctions that are shaky at best) finally peeked out from the ignominious veil of shame and darkness behind which they had hid for generations, and soaked up a bit of daylight. In New York this growth was dominated by the work of three men who, even thirty years after the fact, in the often unforgiving light of retrospect, are still viewed as masters of their milieux: filmmaker and actor Jack Smith, theatrical everyman Charles Ludlam and art-world titan Andy Warhol.

about it is that it's very mixed, and I think that people do come to see the show. Unfortunately, the stage is not quite as great as the Pyramid's was, and it's almost impossible to breathe or to move or to get to the stage or dance—

Flloyd: You can't dance on the stage.

Bunny: You can't dance in the club! You cannot dance on the dance floor.

Julian: It also happens very late.

Miss Understood: Well, everything happens late.

Hapi Phace: Well, we're used to that. That's no problem.

Between the three of them, they would discover the multidimensional appeal and theatrical potential of drag, as well as the enormous power it had to fuel the avant-garde which—thanks to them and their attendant queens—seemed, for a few years anyway, actually to exist.

Interestingly enough, each of these three masters was initially inspired by the same muse, a man whose reputation in the long run never attained even a fraction of the notoriety of the artists whose imaginations he so thoroughly captured. Postal worker by day, drag legend by night, **Mario Montez** "was a good Catholic boy," as Fran Lebowitz recalls, who styled himself after Maria Montez, queen of the 1940s B-movie set. According to Warhol, Jack Smith adored Montez "because he could instantly capture the sympathy of the audience" [POPism, p. 181], while Warhol himself noted that Mario "was one of the best natural comedians I'd ever met. [He] had that classic comedy combination of seeming dumb but being able to say the right things with perfect timing; just when you thought you were laughing at him, he'd turn it all around." [Ibid, 223] Smith, his disciple Warhol and Ludlam would all eventually take advantage of Montez' unpretentious gifts. Their "sharing" of his talents was emblematic of what another member of that uniquely fecund scene, drag star **Agusto Muchado,** would later call the intense "cross-pollination" that took place during that period.

The ball got rolling in earnest in 1963 when Smith's undisputed cinematic masterpiece, *Flaming Creatures,* was released. An hour-long surrealist epic that has been described as everything from a demonic catastrophe to a film about transvestites, it was probably a bit of both. Either way, more than a couple of people were thrown in jail just for screening the movie, which was widely decried as obscene. Obscene or not, it managed to find an uncanny balance between violence and eroticism that was, finally, nothing less than mesmerizing. Disjointed, bizarre, full of

Part III: Drag and Feminism

Julian: What about the whole so-called issue of "Feminism versus Drag." Does anybody care about that?

Miss Understood: Well, I don't think it's a big feminist issue lately.

Bunny: Feminists are too uptight anyway.

Julian: Well, some of "them" actually enjoy drag. Some of the best theory about drag that's been put out there is feminist theory too—

Miss Understood: I agree with a lot of feminist theory.

Bunny: I'm a feminist.

Miss Understood: I think that men in general are pretty misogynist. Men are sexist all the time, and if drag queens are men, of course there's

images of rape, gender confusion and orgiastic intensity, *Flaming Creatures* ended up setting the standard for the next twenty years of avant-garde filmmaking, and made Smith the unwitting father of New York drag as we know it today.

Warhol himself was beginning his own career as a filmmaker and artist, using Montez in his first movies with sound. Captivating as the image of Montez slowly eating a banana or uttering the word "diarrhea" over and over must have been, Warhol's greatest contributions to drag on film would come later in 1968 with the "discovery" of his three drag superstars, **Jackie Curtis, Candy Darling** and **Holly Woodlawn**. These four, in conjunction with the rest of Warhol's infamous Factory, would transform the role of the drag queen in modern American society—from the height of homosexual depravity into the ultimate in hipness, chicness and glamour.

Warhol met both Jackie and Candy on the same day, while walking on Eighth Street in the Village, and soon had them both starring in one of his earliest hits, *Flesh*, directed by Paul Morrissey. The girls were an instant sensation, not only on the screen but on the streets, at the Factory and in the clubs, where they decorated the space and lit up the entire downtown scene. For the first time, really, queens were hot. Celebrities who dropped by Max's Kansas City, a downtown artists' hangout with a notoriously well-peopled back room, would beg to be introduced to them. **Agusto Muchado** gleefully recalls Jane Fonda, "looking very Barbarella," getting up the nerve to cross the room and introduce herself to Jackie.

Holly Woodlawn, the only surviving member of the legendary trio, came on board in 1969, playing opposite Warhol's favorite male star, the remarkably well-endowed Joe Dallesandro, in Warhol and Morrissey's next great collaboration, *Trash*. As if these movies were not enough to memorialize the girls and their trailblazing careers, Lou Reed—also a participant in the Factory scene—in his signature song, "Walk on the Wild Side,"

---

going to be sexist things coming out of their mouths. But drag as a whole—as a thing in itself—I don't really think is sexist. First of all, most drag queens just completely adore anybody that they're emulating. And if you look at the drag queen icons, they're all women who were outrageously powerful. All those old movie stars were strong—

Bunny: Yeah, but I think their icons are different from the way they treat women on a day-to-day basis.

Linda Simpson: But it's true that straight men are much more misogynist than gay men.

Hapi Phace: Oh, I don't know about that. But— All right, children, let Grandma speak. The younger generation has spoken.

Flloyd: Tranma?

Hapi Phace: The Trannie Grannie would like to say something on that issue. The thing that you have to remember is that as drag queens, we

turned them almost into folk heroes writing: "Holly came from Miami, FLA/Hitchhiked her way across the USA/Plucked her eyebrows on the way/Shaved her legs and then he was a she/She says 'Hey, babe, take a walk on the wild side' . . . Candy came from out on the island/In the back room she was everybody's darling/But she never lost her head/Even when she was giving head/She says, 'Hey, babe, take a walk on the wild side' . . . Jackie was just speeding away/Thought he was James Dean for a day/A hustle here and a hustle there/New York City is the place where they say, 'Hey, babe, take a walk on the wild side.' "

Meanwhile, not far away, another one of Warhol's worker bees, one who provided the sound for the earlier Montez pictures, screenwriter Ronnie Tavel was also busy collaborating with John Vaccaro and Charles Ludlam at Vaccaro's Playhouse of the Ridiculous. Also taking their cue from *Siren of Atlantis*, *White Savage* and *Cobra Woman*, Maria Montez's B-grade hits from the 1940s, they were staging their own cross-dressed, low-budget variations on those movies' pulpy, space-age themes. Vaccaro, who had himself appeared in several Jack Smith movies, created theatrical versions that, of course, featured the other omnipresent Montez in starring roles.

Apparently intimidated by the arrests of those who had screened *Flaming Creatures*, Vaccaro chose, in ironic juxtaposition to his plays' lurid themes and counter-culture attitude, to keep the productions relatively conservative, avoiding such ire-inspiring hot potatoes as homosexuality and nudity. This was all too much for the irrepressible thespian **Charles Ludlam,** who in 1967, as the leading voice of dissent within the fractious Ridiculous company, lead a mutiny of sorts, forming his own group and taking with him the bulk of the Playhouse's members, including Tavel, Montez, **Lola Pashalinski** and **Black Eyed Susan**—all of whom would live to congratulate themselves.

---

have a lot of the same issues as feminists in our own dealings in the gay community. To gay men, we're considered "women." We get to see a lot of the misogyny in gay men. I don't know about straight men, but—

Julian: Well, is that misogyny or just a lack of interest?

Bunny: Oh, it's definitely misogynist, the same way that lesbians hate straight men. Hate! Some do. And it might be the same proportion.

But there's some lesbians that just hate straight men.

Miss Understood: Well, they have more of a reason to, though.

Flloyd: That's like the Chelsea muscle queens who hate the drag queens.

Miss Understood: Lesbians have more of a reason. Someone that's been stepped on has more of a reason to hate back, you know,

Renaming themselves the Ridiculous Theatrical Company, they spent the next thirty years forging an entirely new theatrical genre. Led by Ludlam, the single drag performer whom every person who saw him is willing to agree was a certifiable genius, they created such classic fantasies as *The Mystery of Irma Vep*, *The Artificial Jungle*, *How to Write a Play*, *Bluebeard* and, perhaps their greatest triumph, Ludlam's own version of *Camille*. In these sprawling, no-holds-barred productions, virtually all of which he wrote himself—blending history, mythology, literature and vaudeville—Ludlam was invariably the star, not to mention half of the supporting cast. Ludlam possessed an unprecedented talent which also made him, of course, a notoriously difficult character. Ludlam and his company would go on to win the hearts of theatergoers around the world, stunning audiences with their versatility, their confrontational approach to difficult questions and, most importantly, their supreme theatricality. Ludlam's longtime lover and collaborator **Everett Quinton** now stands guard over the Ridiculous legacy, starring in and writing plays, managing the group and seeing the company through to its fourth decade. Since his death in 1987, Ludlam's legacy has only seemed to grow, as history confirms that he was, beyond being merely a gifted drag performer, one of the most singularly original, brilliant and important voices in the history of American theater. With the universality of his lunacy and the virtuosity of his talent, he almost single-handedly dragged drag into the mainstream of American culture.

As if these stilleto strides were not phenomenal enough, there was the little matter, in June of 1969, of the Stonewall Rebellion, three days of unplanned civil disobedience, political protest and general hell-raising by the fed-up patrons of a dimly lit gay bar and their uppity drag queen friends. Not to be confused with their cousins in the theater or Warhol's superstars, this ragtag band of street queens and hustlers, led by sainted queens **Marsha P. Johnson** and **Sylvia (Ray) Rivera,** were no

they're not the ones that caused the problem.

Bunny: But whatever the reason, there's also a kind of gay man that hates women and looks at a woman in a gay bar and says, "Fish." And, Linda, I wish you would stop it!

Chicklet: Well, you know, I can understand how a woman might be offended by that, because if I see a straight person portraying a flaming faggot—

Miss Understood: *To Wong Foo* . . .

Chicklet: If it's done in a way that I think is distasteful, I am offended, but that's not always the case. However, you know, if I'm portraying a woman, or someone who is "womanlike," I try to portray them in a way that I think is fun or empowering. I never put down what it is to be quote-unquote a woman or womanlike. It's never about that.

Bunny: Then there's someone like me, who

strangers to police raids on the mob-owned gay bars of Greenwich Village. On June 28th, only days after the death of gay uber-icon Judy Garland, during what was supposed to have been a routine police raid, the emotionally raw group of otherwise lamblike patrons fought the police tooth and nail. This sparked several days of rioting—made famous in part by the queens' unorthodox use of hair pulling, cat scratching and chorus line kicking—which are now viewed as the official start of the modern gay liberation movement. In several nights of conflicts with the bewildered cops, the resourceful queens threw rocks, bottles and parking meters in a battle that even cops concede went to the queens. In *The Beautiful Room Is Empty*, his coming-of-age story set in New York in the late sixties, novelist Edmund White has one of the battle's veterans reflect upon the riots in a moment that perfectly sums up ten years of monumental movement by a people and a city being led to their destiny, knowingly or otherwise, by drag queens. Surveying the scene outside the bar, the black-and-blue warrior notes with both ruefulness and satisfaction that "Lilly Law never should have fucked with us the night that Judy died."

As the city recovered from the upheaval of the sixties, it headed willy-nilly for the upheaval of the seventies—for drag queens, an upbeat and productive era, only slightly less intense than the previous decade. As the gay liberation movement gathered steam, often in cautious proximity to the growing peace movement, queens started looking more like hippies and vice-versa. Street queens proliferated, spreading a culture of transgression and subversion into the community at large. Muchado recalls that, with certain laws still in place which forbade men from wearing more than three articles of women's clothing, street queens—who made their "livings" hustling, begging and helping one another—made a celebration out of turning something like a button-down shirt into a tight-fitting halter top. In stark contrast to the lives of today's capitalist queens, and consistent with the

wants to wear women's clothes, and I don't care what anyone has to say. If I did, I wouldn't be getting onstage in drag, or leaving my house in drag. I'd be sitting in the dark, jerking off into women's panties like Linda's father does. [Laughter.]

Hapi Phace: Well—I don't know about the other queens around here—I've always admired women, or else I wouldn't want to grow up to be one. You know? And I don't know if I'm successful in being a quote-unquote woman, or actually know what it's like to actually be a uterine-carrying woman.

Bunny: Wooooooo! [Giggles.]

Hapi Phace: I mean, feminist issues like abortion and things like that—in those ways, no, being a queen isn't the same as being a feminist. But all people have those issues of abortion, body rights and things like that. It's really up to the queen. If they're misogynist to begin with, they're misogy-

general socialist ethos of the sixties and seventies, street life for queens, Muchado says, was all about sharing, be it food, shelter or tips on when to grab a cheap pair of panty hose at Klein's. "Money was never an issue," he recalls. "No one ever expected to make any so they were free to do what they pleased as drag queens."

In a sort of intramural cultural exchange, a traveling band of "glitter queens" named the **Cockettes,** famous in their hometown of San Francisco, visited New York for a week of performances off-Broadway in 1971. In retrospect, no one can imagine how this blissed-out group of glorified hippies, resplendent in white makeup, full beards and more glitter than you can shake a stick at, managed to generate the hype they did prior to their arrival. Perhaps it was the advance word spread by the likes of Truman Capote and Rex Reed, who must have fallen under some spell while out west. Muchado recalls, as does Fran Lebowitz, who had the hilarious job of picking the troupe up at the airport (the **Cockettes** *always* traveled in full drag), that in the days before their first performance they were feted, glitter and all, as if they were visiting royalty. At the height of New York's "radical chic" period, anyone who was anyone was fighting for the chance to get a bunch of cross-dressed, tripping hippies up for tea, and for a fleeting couple of days the **Cockettes** were literally the toast of New York high society.

The mirror cracked, however, when the curtain went up. In front of an audience that included the likes of Anthony Perkins, Gore Vidal, Angela Lansbury and Anthony Quinn, the most anticipated performance of the year was a full-fledged debacle. Revealing themselves to be the infantile and orgiastic Haight-Ashbury regulars that they really were, the **Cockettes** thoroughly embarrassed themselves by aimlessly romping about the stage, shouting and singing incoherently and having sex. The audience's many celebrities, too shocked by the enormity of it even to enjoy it as a

nist. It doesn't matter if they wear a dress or not. I mean, there are women who are misogynist.

Linda Simpson: There are some drag queens who are misogynistic, granted, but—

Hapi Phace: And there's a tradition of that in those old Fire Island queens and stuff like that. There's a tradition. Their whole act is that.

Bunny: Yes, there is. Totally. And those are the ones who are only going to go out—who wouldn't

ever want to set foot in a mixed bar—they'd only want to go out to the Ice Palace or Champs, and they'd sneer at a woman that comes in there. There's all kinds of gay bars that don't allow them, that try to make them uncomfortable, because maybe they feel like they had a harder time coming to terms with their own fagdom. They feel that women are held up as what they *should* want, and they *don't* want them. They're out trying to do their gay thing after having "you should want a woman" drummed into their heads their whole

Michael Musto
Gossip Columnist, The Village Voice

Basically, it's a costume, but it's a costume that enables people to tap into their true personalities, because society always demands that we make cut-and-dried distinctions between male and female, and if you're male, supposedly you have to live like a man. But this frees these people. I mean, even when I've done drag, it's just—suddenly you shed all convention. . . . You're free to do whatever you want with it once you have the dress on. But I find that with a lot of these drag queens they're much more beautiful and fabulous in drag, and it seems to tap into this fabulous person inside of them. Whereas as a man a lot of them are kind of schlubby and not exactly the most vibrant people.

cheap, dark thrill, made lots of little beelines for the door. Needless to say, the great **Cockettes** were non grata by sunup. On the upside, however, this represented perhaps the first instance of hometown spirit as it might apply to New York drag queens. That so many swells had shown up at all surely meant that in their collective estimation drag was worthy of attention in the first place, a sentiment obviously fostered by the consistently interesting work of *local* queens. The disappointment over the **Cockettes** was clearly accompanied by an inverse sense that in New York, you've got to do better than this; that no self-respecting New York queen would be caught dead in a calamity like that.

Despite the horror of their adolescent shenanigans, the **Cockettes**—and another similarly inclined West Coast troupe called the **Angels of Light**—did inspire a group of New Yorkers to try their hand at forming what would become a major institution within the drag and Village communities: the **Hot Peaches**. Founded by Jimmy Commecia and a group of actors and street queens, housed in a variety of locations in the east lower digits—one of their first lofts was supplied by Warhol superstar **Jackie Curtis**—the Peaches, who still tour and perform today, mounted what they believed the **Cockettes** had intended to and simply could not. Their first show, *The Wizard of Us*, featured **Zomba,** now a Soho retailer, in the role

lives, and so they *resent* women. I mean, maybe that's why. But maybe it's just a personality thing, one side of the brain competing with the other. But there's definitely a kind of gay man that hates women.

Flloyd: She brought up a good point, which is that I think a lot of gay men hate the femininity inside themselves.

Hapi Phace: Speaking of Chelsea muscle queens.

Flloyd: Yeah. That's why they try so hard to be "real men" and be this thing that real men are supposed to be, and that's probably what a lot of the muscle queens have to do.

Hapi Phace: I mean, that's where the phrase "straight acting, straight appearing" comes from. You know, if you're a homosexual man, why are you looking for this image of *hetero*sexuality, of a straight man?

of Dorothy in a hallucinatory musical send up of the Baum/Flemming classic. Like the work of the Ridiculous Theater Company, the **Hot Peaches** pageants were sprawling, often disorganized and heavy on parody. But like Ludlam's shows, they were literate, steeped in theatricality and buoyed by the imagination and creative energy of the company, which included such drag luminaries as **Minette, Marsha P. Johnson, International Chrysis,** and occasionally **Ethyl Eichelberger**.

Other troupes began popping up as well. Several dancers who had worked with Ludlam formed the Trockadero Gloxina, which would eventually become the **Ballet Trocadero de Monte Carlo,** an all male drag ballet troupe that is one of New York's all-time most successful exports. Toward the end of the seventies Ira Siff's **La Grand Scena Opera,** the vocal equivalent of the Trocadero troupe, also made landfall and has been performing ever since.

As the seventies wore on, New York, ready to believe anything after the insanity of the sixties, warmed up to the more legitimate cultural potential of drag. As the city teetered on the brink of bankruptcy, however, and the Studio 54 crowd (itself rife with queens) burned what was left of the candle at both ends, there was a growing sense of what **Hattie Hathaway,** veteran drag queen and downtown historian, calls *weltschmertz,* "world weariness." The onslaught of AIDS (a tragedy that witnesses assert began in earnest ten years before it gained national notoriety) only added to the sense that the empire was crumbling and, almost in response, the drag scene folded up as the decade came to an end. The cycle had come round again and the city seemed focused on the more sober pursuits of recovering financially and coming to terms with a disease that was eating the citizenry alive—drag queens and civilians alike. But like little menorahs in the dark, indefatigable as ever, many queens continued quietly to ply their trade. The **Hot Peaches** continued to meet with success, as did the

Flloyd: Because it fits in with society.

Hapi Phace: Well, not only that, but also they hate their feminine side. They hate their gayness.

Flloyd: Because it's "wrong."

Part IV: Drag and the Media

Bunny: But *To Wong Foo* . . . was almost like a fairy tale. It didn't need to have sex, I don't think.

Hapi Phace: There was an Australian film that came out—*Priscilla* . . .

Bunny: Which was crap! That I left after twenty

other drag companies and troupes that had sprung up in the previous years. It would not be long before the pendulum would begin its swing back, and drag would once again take center stage in New York and—finally—around the world.

The 80s: Va-Va-Voom

Drag in New York in the eighties was dominated by two East Village clubs, the Pyramid and the Boy Bar. Virtually every queen working in New York today—save for purely theatrical girls like **Charles Busch**—came up through the ranks of one, and even occasionally both, of these two extremely fecund venues. What our increasingly diminished wetlands are to the global food chain, these clubs were to the drag queen ecosystem of New York for fifteen years. There was clearly a sense of competition between the Boy Bar and the Pyramid, but it was softened by a sororal clubbiness—in the same way that Harvard students and Yalies pretend to make a lot of hay about their centuries-old rivalry, all the while knowing that no matter who wins the football game, they are all members of the elite's elite. That same sort of self-conscious finger-poking characterized the decade-long competition between the decidedly artsy, considerably older Pyramid, and her wickedly glamorous little stepsister Boy Bar.

Drag legend **Hattie Hathaway**, a combination Babe Paley and Boris Karloff who was present at the inception of the Pyramid's drag scene, recalls the Anvil, a notorious cabaret, bar and sex club at Fourteenth Street and the West Side Highway. "Sometime in the late seventies or early eighties" she recalls, the Anvil launched a night that catered to New Wave's odd mix of drag, glam, rock and roll and "gender fuck," a postmodern offshoot of drag in which female and male traits are combined to create an effect that

minutes of, and which I thought was . . . I despised *Priscilla*. Sickening.

Miss Understood: You really thought *To Wong Foo* . . . was better than *Priscilla*?

Bunny: I laughed my head off in *To Wong Foo* . . . I walked out after thirty minutes of that other crap.

Hapi Phace: Because of the people in it?

Bunny: No, because I can't bear to see Terence Stamp trying to pass himself off as a transsexual with a full beard! The director never says, "You have to put thing on the lens there, please." He's talking like a fireman, an actor of his caliber. I think if you get your dick and balls cut off, you don't talk like that. Excuse me, you're living as a woman and you've got a full beard and you've been a transsexual for years?

Miss Understood: I've seen a few of those.

is disorienting but, more than anything, just not very much fun to look at. "The Anvil's DJ had a brother who ran 99 Records, an early New Wave label. The New Wave idea was his," recounts Hattie, a walking encyclopedia of these sorts of tidbits. Drag queens were just some of the freaky types hired by the Anvil to generate a feeling of debauchery, intellectualism and hipness, all at the same time. It was a combination that worked for a while. Drag queens on stage, go-go boys on the bar, and, on one particular night that has taken on mythical proportions and remembered fondly if hazily by Hattie, Andy Warhol and his society pals downstairs in the sex club—who could ask for anything more?

Ultimately however, the all-male atmosphere of the West Village sex emporium proved unstimulating for the likes of performers **Tanya Ransom** and **John Kelly,** who became famous for his uncanny tributes to singer/songwriter Joni Mitchell. Ransom and Kelly had been cultivating their unconventional (read too artsy) drag shows in small clubs in SoHo and the East Village, because they found the West Village drag scene too rigid, too traditional and too exclusive of women.

In a move that would place the heart of New York drag back where it all began—only blocks from the Bowery—Ransom and Kelly took their gig to the East Village. From the moment these two began performing at the Pyramid in 1981, with fellow drag performer **Sister Dimention,** the place basically exploded, swiftly becoming the center of downtown nightlife for almost ten years. Artists, writers, actors, movie stars, fashion people and drag queens were all part of a scene that catered to every freaky taste in the book, and which is said to have made a hefty bundle of cash. **The "Lady" Bunny, Hapi Phace, Lypsinka, Tabboo!, Lahoma, RuPaul, Flloyd, Linda Simpson, Ebony Jett, Chicklet, Misstress Formika, Miss Understood** and **Afrodite** are just some of the Pyramid's illustrious alumni from the last fourteen years. Many remained

Bunny: Gimme a break. That tells me that there's an *idiot* in charge of the movie. And the jokes were so lame and stale. The jokes in *To Wong Foo* . . . had me hooting! People were looking around at me thinking, What is she on?

Miss Understood: Would you rather ask Ann-Margret to play that Terence Stamp part?

Bunny: I wish they had. Because I could not believe that. Plus that there was not one likable lead in it. I despised those—I'm not even going to say it. I hated those characters. I thought they looked like insidious, bratty, tired, bitchy queens.

Miss Understood: I thought they were three-dimensional.

Bunny: When with *To Wong Foo* . . . , the whole gist of it is: You may have considered these things freaks in the past, but you dull old Americans with your backward ways need to wake up!

fiercely faithful to the club, serving as managers, hosts and impresarios, while others merely used it as a launching pad for larger and scarier careers.

The Pyramid enjoyed a near perfect location on Avenue A between Sixth and Seventh, on the edge of the infamous Alphabet, in New York's Lower East Side. Across the street from the notorious Tompkins Square Park, it was on the very border between what many reckoned to be reasonably safe and what was known as a veritable black hole of crime, drugs and bombed-out tenements; perfect for weeding out the sorts of welter-weight clubgoers the Pyramid crowd would have detested anyway. Furthermore, the building featured several architectural elements that made it, either by fate or design, a sublime space in which to promote and feature drag. A long, narrow bar area led to a larger, more square dance floor, which had at its far end an elevated stage; all in all, the entire establishment couldn't hold more than a few hundred people. Behind and leading down from the stage was what could nominally be called a staircase but was really a ladder that only Hitchcock could have invented and upon which many a queen nearly lost her life—at the very least. The precipitous descent lead to a dressing room and basement area that eventually became part of the public space. The layout of the Pyramid allowed patrons uninterested in the performance to hang out and drink in the bar area without interrupting the action on stage, while the dressing room area, remote as it was, provided what more than a few queens have described as the essential element in the club's success as a drag venue: a private haven for queens. In its cramped embrace, performers could escape the throngs of admirers who apparently left them no peace. Furthermore, in stark contrast to the monster discos of today, this private space was where queens met, gossiped and shared news of the trade. It is important to note that the current lack of this sort of sanctuary is sighted all too often by queens as among the most disappointing facts of modern drag life.

Miss Understood: I thought it was drag positive.

Bunny: —and see that these things can decorate a room in a jiffy, to the tune of "Wonder Woman," they can straighten you out in some of your misconceptions about how—whatever.

Miss Understood: Linda said, "Now we're all going to feel like we have to go out and save the world." They expect so much of us now.

Julian: What's more, a lot of the larger audience out there, whoever they may be, who could make a legitimate star out of a drag queen, don't know where to go to watch drag. They don't know where to latch on and become a fan.

Bunny: Well, then they're *stupid*. And that's the whole thing about mainstream people: they're stupid, you know? Most people are just ignorant.

Of course, the "performances" were rarely limited to the stage area. Go-go dancing drag queens (supposedly a first) were all over the bar, and many of the patrons themselves were eager participants in the general lunacy. There was little formal differentiation between audience and performers. On any given night, **Hattie** might be staging one of the spectaculars that earned her the early sobriquet Loretta B. DeMille—a passion play that might feature John Sex and Wendy Wild—while **Tabboo!**'s increasingly valuable artwork festooned the walls and ceilings of the entire club. **Ethyl Eichelberger** and **Hapi Phace** might be dancing on the bar as hundreds of customers, high on the heady combination of hard drugs and harder atmosphere, dressed in everything from gold body paint to full drag to perhaps nothing at all, milled about, filling the coffers of a club that would almost single-handedly sustain the entire downtown drag queen community for close to a decade.

It was into the Pyramid that the first load of Atlanta queens spilled in 1983. Who at the time could have known that **RuPaul, Lahoma, The "Lady" Bunny** and **Flloyd** would rise to become something of a drag queen mafia, that they would as a group innervate the scene as they eventually did or that **RuPaul** would become, in fact, a household name? Who could have guessed that late in the summer of 1984, tired, broke and bored, they would mount a makeshift drag festival in the dangerous shadows of the Tompkins Square band shell that would become *Wigstock*, the single largest celebration of drag in the world—ever.

This was the Pyramid. In its time it would be home to **Hapi Phace**'s *Whispers* and *Back Door*, two evenings that were so successful they have assured Hapi a place in the annals of performance art history; *Channel 69*, **Linda Simpson**'s ridiculous knockoff of network television which introduced a stunning number of up-and-coming queens to the audience that would eventually adore them, and *The Ball*, **Miss Understood**'s weekly

---

Miss Understood: They need control.

Flloyd: They do what they're told.

Bunny: Seek and ye shall find. They do what they're told, they buy what they're sold. They're idiots.

Linda Simpson: The thing is, too, RuPaul is incredible—and I think she really *likes* what she does—but really, deep down, I don't think I'd want to compromise as much as Ru has had to.

Bunny: She really likes what she does?

Linda Simpson: Yeah, I think so.

Bunny: On a track date, when she has to perform "Supermodel" every single time like Gloria Gaynor does? I don't see how.

Linda Simpson: You're right, she may not like the specifics, but I think she likes the stardom of it, you know.

Bunny: But the actual show?

drag bash, which closed with the demise of the club as a venue for drag in 1995. In between these weekly staples were literally countless productions, parties and performances that highlighted the drag community's boundless energy, nutty inventiveness and lasting appeal.

Meanwhile, just a few blocks to the west, on the hellish strip mall that is St. Marks Place between Second and Third avenues—closer to civilization many might say—another Southerner was cooking up a plan to rescue New York drag from what he believed was an artsy rut. A UCLA dropout, twenty-year-old **Matthew Kasten** came to New York in the early eighties to style hair. Before he left, he would fecund an entire generation of New York's most glamorous drag queens, their outfits and the very way in which they saw themselves.

"My mother used to take me shopping," Kasten recalls. "She would point to things and say to me 'This is good taste, this is not,' and things like 'Always buy Baccarat, never Lalique. Who needs a crystal pineapple anyway?'" Like mother like son. In that same spirit, he remembers that "the Pyramid just wasn't glamorous enough for me. I'm from the South, where pageants are the thing. So I gave the managers of Boy Bar a proposal for a beauty pageant."

According to Kasten, those managers were pushing him to use Pyramid queens, but that was precisely the point. He wanted to create his own vision with his own girls; Busby Berkeley on a budget. But as soon as the announcement was made in the clubs that a new drag venue was opening, the queens "came running." Kasten's infamous pickiness, however, was apparent from the get-go, and of the many who applied he remembers being able "to scrape together four girls and two pairs of shoes." **Connie Girl, Glamamore, Shannon** and **Chandelier** were the guinea pigs in a performance that will not go down in history as a night of great drag. But Kasten had yet to discover the talent that would eventually make his show the hottest in town.

Flloyd: I think Ru likes having the security of knowing what is expected of him.

[Big pause.]

Linda Simpson: Oh really?

Flloyd: Yeah. I think Ru likes to have the product and know that "this is what I'm selling, and this is what I'm pushing." Like the whole book tour. I don't think he had any problem with that. I think he enjoyed selling the book, knowing he was making money off featuring the book and talking about the book endlessly. I think he likes having the product and pushing the product.

Linda Simpson: Ru's cleverer than she comes off on a lot of those stupid talk shows, because they're all scripted and they ask such dumb questions about her getting ready and stuff. That would be kind of a drag—excuse the pun—after a while, to kind of suddenly dumb down yourself for a general market.

"That year," he says, "Brooks Van Horne, the famous costume house, went out of business and they had a bag sale. Ten bucks a bag." Kasten and friends came up with hundreds of matching sets of costumes for three people each. The winners were three sailor suits from *Dames at Sea* by Madame Bertha. In a scene right out of *Summer Stock,* each of the queens in turn revealed the unique talent that would be her contribution to putting the show over the top. Kasten could style wigs like nobody's business, **Glamamore** could sew to beat the band, and **Connie Girl** (whom Kasten says he first saw "walking down Ninth Street dressed like Christie Brinkley in a pale blue bathing suit, amazing") could tap. Who knew? Earnestly comingling their various gifts, the kids quickly mounted a huge Americana number featuring the altered costumes, a set complete with stars and stripes and **Glamamore** as Kate Smith singing "God Bless America." "That was it," Kasten says with typical modesty. "We went right over the top. From then on, that was what we did. The Pyramid had no choice but to bow down to us."

What the Boy Bar Beauties (as they would come to be known) also did, at the insistence of their czarish leader, was lip-sync. While the girls at the Pyramid, who were ruled by no central authority, did basically whatever the hell they wanted, the Boy Bar girls were always mute, opening their mouths only to mime prerecorded performances by a recognizable stable of gay-identified disco divas. The only performer who ever actually spoke on the Boy Bar stage was Kasten himself, who, as emcee, showed about as much patience for his audience as he did for his "children's" various sartorial shortcomings. Nevertheless, the recipe was working and the Boy Bar Beauties became an overnight sensation—in three weeks. To the performers at the Pyramid, who were clearly wishing for failure in the west, there would be no more shots across the bow. The two clubs commenced an almost ten-year competition that, while known occasionally to get nasty, proved productive for both. The

Miss Understood: That's what kills me about being mainstream in anything. I'm sick of these talk shows. They don't look into anything. They're surfacy, surfacy, surfacy: "Oh, look at that! Oh, let me walk in those shoes." And this is Rolonda talking. "I gotta get makeup tips from you girls. Ho, ho, ha, ha." And they don't stop and talk about anything or really ask you what your life is really about.

Bunny: Rolonda is an idiot. She's an *idiot!* She's looking at her cue cards! The minute that she's asked you a question, she looks to see the next question. She doesn't even listen to one word of your answer, to delve into anything deeper, because she's an idiot. You can tell that by her voice, her dic-tion. [Laughter.]

Miss Understood: I know her show is only an hour, but when they have those goddamn family problems where someone fucked someone's uncle, they'll sit there and talk about every little detail.

spirit of competition spurred each "house" to greater creative heights and to define its style as sufficiently different from the other to quell any fears that they might split the available audience. Several queens made a habit of performing in both clubs, a practice that in time ceased even to raise an eyebrow. Ultimately, a city that had lacked a consistent drag club for nearly ten years turned out in throngs to see shows in both venues, eager perhaps to counteract the dullness of queenless nightlife, an increasing emphasis on big muscles and the inevitable stupefaction that is the result of years of unyieldingly bad music played too loudly.

Kasten began to develop a reputation for treating his beauties with an objectivity that could border on meanness. The Boy Bar Beauties were, however, absolutely subject to his will, which, after the fact, most of them are quick to note was all for the best. While he may not have been the sweetest producer they could have imagined, he turned many a confused young man into a glamorous icon. "**Candis Cayne** is probably my prime example," he instructs. "She started out as this bearded boy," he says of a queen who today is, in drag parlance, as "cunty" as they come. "That white foundation was so horrible. She looked like the Joker!" A more neutral base, redder hair and a tighter-fitting outfit, however, and a transformed Candis was soon being crowned Miss Boy Bar. **Perfidia, Mona Foot, Flotilla De Barge, Sweetie, Miss Guy,** and **Raven-O** are but a few of the more famous performers who came up through Matthew Kasten's particular school of glamour drag.

What with Pyramid and Boy Bar, two drag locomotives churning ahead at full steam, each fueled by the other's success, the downtown community was waking up to drag. Emboldened by their new popularity, many queens began striking out on their own. Some took to the local cable airwaves, some of which had been reserved by the city for people just like them. Subsidiary drag companies were formed. Queens suddenly were hip! Party pro-

Bunny: [Imitating Rolonda.] "Do you know that this is per-son-al-ly the way that you would han-dle this sit-u-a-tion here?" [Laughter.] You can tell by Rolonda's dic-tion that she's ab-so-lute-ly out of her mind. Just the way that she speaks to people. She has that o-ver-dic-tion. She's an *idiot*.

Linda Simpson: Well, when we were on, she had to start it.

Bunny: She's an *idiot*!

Flloyd: Ru was on Lauren Hutton.

Miss Understood: Did they talk intelligently?

Bunny: *That* is the most despicable show of them all! Oh, how I curse that snaggletooth bitch!

Hapi Phace: But you haven't seen *Carnie*.

Bunny: Oh no, I haven't.

Flloyd: But Ru said that his interview on Lauren

moters began hiring them to populate their events, just to be there—"a freak on a box," as **Hapi Phace** would later describe it.

The city as a whole began embracing its queens as it hadn't done since Warhol first made them chic in the sixties. Swiss import Suzanne Bartsch, the mother of all party promoters, hired drag queens to work her parties at the Copacabana on the east side in 1988. As popular as they had become below 14th Street, most queens were perfect strangers to the upper crust of Manhattan's social scene. But the voracious and rapacious eighties were as good a time as any to introduce the two worlds, which is precisely what Bartsch did.

"I took it out from the underground. I made it acceptable in the corporate world," she says, sounding rather like a fay Arnold Schwarzenegger. "Corporate parties call me up and ask me to send some drag queens over," she remarks. "The Love Ball was the first major event where the people were spending thousands of dollars to watch the show. It was an AIDS benefit. They had a lot of the drags serving and pouring champagne. It was a brilliant feeling and created a great energy. I like the spirit of the drag queens." And she couldn't have hated the fortune she was making bringing them to her corporate clients. To her credit, though, not only did she open up an entirely new market for queens to pillage, but even her biggest detractors (Kasten calls her "the thieving magpie") will swear by her honesty and willingness to pay top dollar. She also upped the stock of her favorite queens by taking them to gigs in other countries in Europe and Asia, giving them a chance to plant seeds in places where a popular queen can make *big* bucks. Lately, Bartsch has put her money where her mouth has been, hiring faithful queens from her coterie to baby-sit her child by diminutive gym owner David Barton.

Explaining the inspiration behind bringing queens uptown on a professional basis, Suzanne Bartsch says, "I love the whole feeling of drag because

Hutton was the most satisfying interview he'd ever done. Although I didn't see it.

Hapi Phace: Well, Lauren is drag-familiar. I mean, she's hung out with drag queens.

Bunny: It's got the most disgusting format I've ever laid eyes on.

Miss Understood: It's a little distracting to watch.

Bunny: It's pathetic, just to take all the meat out of the subject and put all the emphasis on the style of the pathetic MTV-influenced wiggling camera. Because *idiots* can't sit and watch a picture of someone and listen to what they're saying. They've got to be veering around.

Miss Understood: I watched it the other day, they had a mirror next to the person. It would go from the TV screen to the person to the mirror, so that sometimes you'd see the reflection of the

they are having fun. I like the idea that the guys are putting on a dress. Why not? I like that they don't have a hang-up about it. I like the whole spirit about it. I like the creativity, because they are able to make something out of nothing. You just know they will turn it out for you. It's theater really. The fact that it's called drag, and it's a man in a skirt, because society says that men should be in pants and women in dresses, so what. It's really theater at the end of the day. So I was attracted to the colorfulness, the spirit, the energy, and I have fun. I love the creativity that goes with it."

By the late eighties, riding a wave that soon threatened to swallow the city wholesale, queens were becoming de rigueur at parties and openings all over town. Talk show producers discovered the ratings bonanza that came with trotting out any guy in a wig willing to humiliate himself in front of millions for free. Gossip columns and party pages were never without a bold-faced drag queen grinning maniacally over the shoulder of some tolerant socialite trying admirably to pretend she knew what the dickens was going on. While the folks in some nameless middle-American township may only now be waking up to the idea of drag, New York has spent the last ten years reeling from an embarrassment of queenly riches. It is a wonder that more New Yorkers, a crabby and fickle crowd to begin with, haven't been out picking off drag queens like so many space invaders.

Strangely, though, the city's appetite for drag now only continues to grow. Queens are out hosting parties, emceeing contests and drawing crowds into clubs and bars from one end of the state to the other. The city's gay nightlife papers, *HomoXtra* and *Next* (strange little get-to-the point 'zines that advertise the parties and clubs that are thrown by the paper's publishers), became essential to navigating the late night scene. These mini-magazines allow queens who otherwise had no way effectively to promote their events a direct line to the very people who comprise the bulk of their audience. It seems a promoter can hardly invite his friends

person in the mirror on the one side and the TV screen of the person is on the other, so therefore it switches from color to black and white and reverse—

Bunny: That's for a generation of people that grew up listening to Walkmans while walking beside each other. The *idiot* wave. When will it end?

Miss Understood: Speaking of talk shows, I was watching that horrible *Charles Perez* the other day. Miss Perez had on "You're a Hag in Drag So You Need a Makeover." The drag queens would bring their friends up. And what was funny was that Tattie went on, who's a real woman! And she passed herself off as a drag queen for a while, till someone blew her cover. And they hated her because she looked like a freak. They thought she was a drag queen. And this woman in the back was so angry at everything. She was going "You do not look like a woman, and these ladies over here"—pointing at these really boring drag queens next to her—

over for dinner unless a queen is serving punch or providing halftime entertainment. In ten short years, New York has become drag city. The country would soon be next.

The Queening of America

In order to understand the moment when drag finally pierced the membrane that, like the one that separates dreams from reality, protects the majority of citizens from learning what city folk have known for some time, one must acknowledge the hegemonic relationship of New York to the rest of the country in terms of popular culture. Manhattan is the great syringe through which the sometimes interesting, often soporific and rarely enriching serum of up-to-the-minute ideas and images is injected into the body of the country as a whole. The process however can be lugubrious. What takes five to ten years to bubble up from New York's own subconscious requires yet another five to ten to begin to be distributed to the hundreds of millions of consumers between the coasts. The fabulously wealthy young creative directors and media analysts who push the plunger of the syringe are themselves slow first to see what's hot, and then slower still to risk making it available to the rest of the country. By the mid-eighties, however, drag finally established a firm enough foothold in the imaginations of New York's media elite to hint that it might be ripe for commodification. Several coinciding factors, some profound, some rather silly, might also have presaged the drag explosion that by the early nineties would scatter its glittery effluvia throughout the Western World.

The primary force that seems to have succeeded in familiarizing the better part of the populace with the image of drag, one can easily believe, has been cable television. The last decade has seen a truly breathtaking

"these ladies over here, they look good. They look good and you, you can't even hang out in the Village looking like that." I'm thinking, Yeah, 'cause people like you come to the Village and yell at everybody. I was just horrified! Obviously, I don't dress like a real woman, and I just don't think that that's what it's about. As drag gets popular, they keep trying to present it that way to take the edge off of it and take everything interesting out of it, and I think that *is* a drag queen.

Chicklet: Well, remember that girl at the Mark Wahlberg show that screamed at us, "Well, you can't buy a uterus!"

Miss Understood: She said it to me. She said, "You can buy all that, but you can't buy a uterus!"

Flloyd: You can buy a uterus. They have those medical catalogs.

Miss Understood: I was gonna say, "Yeah, after

widening of that avenue of information distribution throughout the nation, making it ever more possible for urban, suburban and even rural Americans to share the same pop-cultural vocabulary. Like the vascular system of a newborn baby, the conduits have been laid at an astonishing rate, connecting vastly disparate locales and enabling the instant transmission of limitless information. The easy availability of ideas and images clearly began to level the playing field of cultural discourse, rendering increasingly obsolete the notion of the benighted country bumpkin, uninformed and unable to become so about the people, places and things so central to urban life.

What this sprawling infrastructure also created, however, was an enormous vacuum; boundless connectivity, but little to deliver. All the channels one could imagine, it turned out, were fairly useless with nothing to show. The beast is a hungry one, perfectly willing to eat its own tail, if that's what it takes to come up with a little something diverting for people to watch. Entire networks were quickly assembled around recycled programming: the kitschy sitcoms of the sixties, or thirty years of nature documentaries; it made little difference. But program developers have always known that cannibalism eventually produces a diminished return. New material was required, and as demand grew to outweigh supply, content that might have been considered totally unacceptable twenty years ago suddenly had its own dedicated channel.

The success of MTV and its many little siblings proved that substance wasn't important; style was sufficient to attract both viewers and sponsors. As the worlds of fashion, television, music and advertising began to collapse in upon themselves, the demand for new *stuff* led prospectors deeper and deeper into the heart of New York's increasingly adolescent, but supersexy nightlife. The youthful exuberance and limitless creativity of the club atmosphere must have been to network demographers what the diamond

I kill you, I'll slit you open and take yours." I was going to say it, but I thought of it later.

Bunny: Well, it's only twenty bucks to get into your mama's!

◢ Part V: Bringing Drag to the Masses

Julian: Okay, let me ask you a couple of questions in terms of getting drag to a broader audience. You just said it was a "mixed" crowd and you liked that, but I think a lot of straight people—that, I assume, being what you mean by "mixed"—feel a little left out of a lot of the gay inside jokes that drag uses, and a lot of the profanity that drag uses.

mines of Cape Hope were to the Dutch. In their thrall, a network program-
mer (or savvy pop star for that matter) would eventually have to encounter
the drag phenomenon in one form or another; enough to be able to see it
for the camera-ready commodity it turned out to be. Eventually came near
the end of 1990.

An unlikely ideological axis formed around the near simultaneous
release of two fiercely original, yet inextricably linked pieces of art: Madonna's "Vogue" video, directed by video visionary David Fincher, and Jennie
Livingston's superb documentary *Paris Is Burning*. The rise to number one
of Madonna's single "Vogue," which would eventually become the corner-
stone of the otherwise mediocre *I'm Breathless,* the soundtrack to *Dick
Tracy,* put the singer at what was (and remains) arguably the very pinnacle
of her career. At a time when the notion of her becoming any more famous
might have seemed impossible, the song and its brilliant video seemed to
put her over the top—into the unique position of being able to disseminate
whatever images she chose to unprecedented masses of consumers the
world over. This time the image would be drag, and no A&R vice president
would have dared instruct Madonna to do anything short of precisely what
she wanted to. In an unparalleled instance of hat tipping, then, Madonna
used the "Vogue" video to reveal the very essence of the appeal that she
had co-opted to make herself into the unrivaled superstar of her era: drag.

Throughout the video, Madonna is seen, in explicit summation of her
entire career, dressed up to resemble a number of screen sirens from Hollywood's golden era. Interestingly, she never manages, and perhaps never
tries, to look precisely like any one star in particular. Recognizable elements of different luminaries are everywhere: Veronica Lake's trademark
veil of hair over the eye; Joan Crawford's hair-in-a-turban (perhaps more
Dunaway than Crawford); Garbo's heavy lids, like half-open storm shutters
over her eyes. The effect of this series of glamorous—and campy—trans-

Hapi Phace: Yeah, like straight people don't use profanity.

Julian: Well, I may be wrong but, for example, Joey Arias has a tendency to—while working all these gorgeous outfits and this extraordinary voice of Billie Holiday's—

Bunny: He does?

Hapi Phace: Where?

Bunny: Wheeeeee! [Giggles.]

Julian: Then, in the middle of the act, in the mid-dle of a Billie Holiday song, he'll start fellating the microphone or making farting noises.

Miss Understood: But that's the *edginess* of it. I don't want to lose that. The problem is—I know everyone keeps kind of making fun of me because I've been going on these TV shows and doing all those videos and stuff, and I'm doing it because it's work and I can get away with it—

formations, during which the singer's disembodied voice is heard directing the listener to follow suit (so to speak), is to reveal her, finally—for all those who hadn't gotten it during the previous ten years—to be a practicing drag queen; a chunky Italian girl who "got it" about the power of trying on a different habit.

The key element in the video is the inclusion of actual queens from the now famous drag balls of Harlem, the setting in which vogueing first emerged. Although none of them is seen in drag per se, their overt effeminacy and "shady" demeanor, coupled with their expert vogueing, reveals them to be precisely that. In turning the camera on this flamboyant and charismatic group of dancers and performers, Fincher and Madonna achieved several momentous tasks at once. Clearly, for the dancers themselves, two of whom—Jose Guitierez and Luis Camacho—eventually went on to tour with Madonna and release their own record, she fulfilled the fantasy that is at the heart of vogueing. The dance is all about transforming one's alienation from life's finer gifts, from the sorts of financial, physical and romantic rewards that fully enfranchised members of our culture are supposedly awash in. By striking the poses of those happy few, by emulating the high-gloss, fashion-magazine version of that fantasy, with all of the archness and irony that one can muster, the voguer enjoys both the fleeting pleasure of living it for a blessed minute or two, while at the same time reaping the special satisfaction that only mockery can bring. Whether or not the fantasy of super-model beauty and choking affluence is a paper tiger, the dance is a sort of incantation, designed to call it up and live it out. It is a bitchy dance. When Madonna came around, however, bearing the opportunity to make the dream a reality, when the rain dance actually brings rain, or in this case a deluge, all bets are off. The dancer becomes the dance.

More important, however, is the extent to which by singing a song

Bunny: I wish you'd get *away* with it!

Miss Understood: —and I can pull it off, but the part that bothers me is that we lose so much of what we're really about. I mean, when they're doing that stupid *New York Undercover* where they were dressing as drag queens and going to a club—

Flloyd: With beards.

Miss Understood: With beards! They're like a watered-down version of what it's all about. They make it seem like it's all about "Oh, we all dress up like girls!" and it's so much more than that. If anybody is going to get mainstream famous again, it won't be a big singer like RuPaul. Maybe it'll be a comedian. And maybe if it's a comedian, it will be somebody who's a little bit edgy and different and that's why they'll get famous. Joan Rivers was filthy and she got famous, and Andrew Dice Clay was filthy and he got famous, so there's no reason that—

about drag, and by explicitly revealing its gay essence, Madonna revealed the secret behind not only her own insanely successful formula, but that of the generations of fabulous stars she invoked in the course of the video: that fabulousness—that strange calculus of beauty, narcissism and camp—is a *queer* conceit and drag is its quintessence. In one broad stroke, she suggests that all of what our culture has conceived of as glamorous and sublime about the female form stems from the strangely idealizing imagination of the many gay men, most of them closeted, who invented and cultivated it. Femininity, and its more severe stepsister glamour, in this way, are simple constructs which can be used oppressively or, as the song hopes, as a means of personal liberation. What the song and video suggest is that the drag queen, by gaining control over the accessories that comprise the glamorous and the "feminine," (1) rescues these items from the hands of oppressors and (2) provides a method for achieving a personal sense of goodwill.

What is important about the message conveyed in the "Vogue" video is Madonna's assertion of her own queenliness and her debt to the gay male subculture that codified it, making it possible for her to learn and exploit it. By fixing America's attention on her fierce, vogueing underlings, she pulled back the curtain to reveal the kinds of men who had lurked behind the scenes practically forever, manufacturing the heightened ideals of so-called womanhood that, through repetition and tacit cultural agreement, had come practically to replace authentic versions of women; people who, as **Miss Understood** remarks, looked a lot more like boys or lesbians than anything drag or Hollywood had to offer. Since the medium is the message, Madonna is seen in the video only as a creature of success; a self-activated, autocratic siren who took the lessons of drag queens to heart and reaped their many rewards. For her, the fantasy dance worked, and the recipe was now for sale. The video's message, then, was that if drag

Julian: Is there anybody about whom you all can come to a consensus—in the New York drag world—who seems likely to be the next big, famous person?

Flloyd: Faux. [Laughter.]

Bunny: Rendella! [Shrieking laughter.]

Flloyd: Rita Menu! [Laughter.]

Bunny: No, thanks, I just lost my appetite! [Continuous laughter.]

Linda Simpson: Let's see, is there anyone?

Miss Understood: You want to know the people I think—and this has nothing to do with my personal likes or dislikes—this is just from who I think is getting visibility in certain things, and I think might get somewhere—it would be Misstress, Hedda and Varla.

Linda Simpson: Misstress, Hedda and Varla?!

Hapi Phace: I think Varla, *maybe*.

vogueing equals personal liberation, and liberation equals success, then drag is the way to free the soul and look great at the same time, be it on the dance floors of Harlem or on stadium-sized stages.

If "Vogue" was the cultural text that poked a hole in the sheath that was stretched between the straight establishment and the drag queen underworld, then *Paris Is Burning* became its subtext. For billions who saw "Vogue," there was considerable ambiguity regarding who the dancers were and what precisely they represented. *Paris Is Burning* answered those questions with no degree of uncertainty. Ingeniously opening up the polyglots, sexualities and cultural codes of the Harlem drag balls and their denizens, the film firmly established the astonishing poetics of alienation, subversion and redemption inherent in the battles royale at the center of the balls.

The combination of high style, athletic vogueing and gender reorganization featured at the balls (and by extension in the more mainstream dance clubs where the same dancers could often be found) must have been irresistible to Madonna, notorious for her keen and voracious appetite for provocative fodder. As if there were any doubt left about the meaning of Madonna's video, several of the dancers who appeared in it were also featured in vicious vogueing battles in Livingston's film (which, while it was released after "Vogue," was filmed, for the most part, before). The cumulative effect of the two sociologically intense works, each illuminating and dramatizing the other, was to tell the story of drag on a large and popular scale. The ingredients for the mass consumption of drag had been available for years, but getting it done would require a trojan horse that no one less iconic or intrepid than Madonna could have built.

Homoeroticism, gay style, and their relationship to culture at large are not radical topics by any means. Never before, however, had drag received the imprimatur of the biggest star in the world in an unsolicited and unam-

---

Julian: Varla's pulling in huge crowds.

Hapi Phace: I don't see why Bunny hasn't been by now.

Linda Simpson: Bunny gets more crowds than anybody.

Hapi Phace: I know, but I don't see why she hasn't *hit*, gone *over*. I mean, I'm not saying that to flatter her 'cause she's sitting here. I really think that. I mean, she's hilarious—

Linda Simpson: What about Lypsinka?

Hapi Phace: Well, Lypsinka is not a gay performer.

Flloyd: Well, I hate to say this but Bunny has an incredible voice. Have you ever heard her sing? [Laughter.]

Hapi Phace: Incred— She's— Well, I mean—

Flloyd: Those of us who saw *Shazzork*—

biguous way. From there, it would be a considerably smaller leap for Tommy Boy Records to sign **RuPaul,** the performer whose enormous success would eradicate any remaining doubts about the mainstream acceptability of drag.

RuPaul herself had struggled long and hard in the drag trenches before she found the "overnight success" that would make her an international star. Her friends from Atlanta all remember an ambitious self-promoter who, even when her product was trashy and vile, would plug and push it until she got it across. Her contract with a major Rap label, odd as it may have seemed, was the natural climax to a life that was intensely focused on success and stardom. It may have been a risk, but Tommy Boy's Monica Lynch, already an adventuresome executive, obviously understood the lessons of Madonna's success. The time had clearly come. Rescuing the subtext of Livingston's film and turning it into the primary message, **RuPaul**'s dance hit and accompanying video "Supermodel of the World" forever changed the face of drag in America. For months during 1993 the airwaves were full to bursting with the sights and sounds of the almost eight-foot drag star, prancing through a Diana Ross–inspired fantasy of the girl from the projects who becomes queen of the worlds of fashion and music. MTV gave her plenty of airtime, and the song scored as more than an average cross-over hit.

RuPaul wisely cleaned up her act before taking it to the masses. As she herself explains in her recent autobiography, the off-color antics that got her noticed in the first place didn't exactly jibe with the "Everybody say 'Love'" routine that she took on tour in late 1993. The mainstreaming of drag has meant the excision of its edginess, a situation that many queens admit that they dread, but would likely get over if the possibility of making a small fortune were within reach. After all, though **RuPaul** may have had to stop aping anal sex to go national, the overnight deluge of cash she received

---

Hapi Phace: *Shazzork* was faaaabulous!

Bunny: Well, it's 'cause I'm lazy and I'm retarded.

Hapi Phace: Well, she gets it from Wigstock, but it's kind of like Halloween: once a year. You know, they hand it over, but then it's like "You freak! Now go back. We're going to come, we're going to monopolize you, we're going to stare at you, we're going to send in camera crews to watch you get dressed, we're going to follow you the whole day, we're going to make a movie, and then we're going to star What's-her-name Arquette's brother. We're going to forget you." That's what's so weird about drag. We go on and do this whole thing, and then they get Robin Williams to play a drag queen in the movie. They take all the gayness out.

Bunny: But you know, we enjoy the edge. I mean, it's important to keep the edge, it's important to keep myself interested.

Quentin Crisp
Author, Social Critic

I think that femininity is something that people feel because it's being shown to them in their family life. But you see, it'll die out because in your lifetime, everyone will be born in a little shallow glass dish, and will be looked after by a man in a white coat with rimless spectacles and white hair, who never says, "And after all I've done for you!" And that will be wonderful . . . Fashion is for people who have no sense of style. Now, the dress of cruelty—the leather and the studs. If I'd been told when I was young that there was a tavern in the town where the brave and the cruel were gathered together, I would have run all the way there. And I would have gone up to the largest and leatheriest of the denizens and I would have said, "If you love me, kill the bartender." And they wouldn't do it! They're standing there squeaking with leather, whistling with studs, talking about the ballet! . . . Your clothes are one way of telling the world who you are. The whole point of style is to cut away all the deadwood in human relationships. Nobody ever talks to me about the weather. Everyone who lives in Manhattan—all those people—they're here for one reason: so as to be ready to rule the world should the opportunity arise.

in return probably more than offset the blow to her artistic integrity. Many queens, of course, harbor dreams of making it as big, but few seem to have worked out how they'll find major backing and distribution, or how they'll work around the scatological humor that makes up a huge percentage of their work. God knows why record companies feel the country is willing to purchase literally millions of copies of Snoop Doggy Dog's albums, in which the rap star details with excruciating clarity the pleasures associated with licking his balls, but reckon that those same consumers would have no interest in hearing, say, **Mona Foot** do the same. Maybe the buying public is just not ready.

At any rate, the question begs asking: now that drag has gone "legit," just how far can it go? What sorts of venues do superstar drag queens play? Will the public at large pay good money to see **Linda Simpson** play emcee to an evening of **Afrodite** and **Candis Cayne** as they lip-sync and shimmy? Does **Chick-**

Linda Simpson: But, Bunny, you would have been so good as Mrs. Doubtfire. [Laughter.]

Bunny: And you would have been so good as her daughter!

Hapi Phace: Well, that's a bad example, because that's a thing where they took *all* the gayness out. I didn't even see it. I wouldn't even go to *Woo Fong Moo,* or whatever, because they're going to take all the gayness out of it. So why are these straight men dress-

ing— I mean, I know one's *supposed* to be a transsexual—

Miss Understood: They're supposed to be gay.

Flloyd: I could imagine Candis Cayne becoming really popular in the straight world, because she's very inoffensive.

Bunny: She's beautiful.

Flloyd: And she's very, like, unsexual.

let really stand a chance of winning one, let alone three, Emmy awards, and if so for what, *Color Me Chicklet, A Happening in Tompkins Square Park*? Will there ever come a day when talented little children will dream of growing up and becoming the next **Sweetie** or **Sissy Fit**?

RuPaul had several things going for him that may not come around again soon: an opening in the cultural landscape that somehow permitted him an entree into the public's imagination, a plan in place for that very eventuality and, perhaps most importantly, a sense of ambition that, by all accounts, could stop Godzilla dead in his tracks. That combination represents an alignment of elusive elements that occurs maybe once a decade, and even then it was just good fortune that **RuPaul** had the goods to deliver. The point has also been raised by a number of observers that when drag goes mainstream, when it is sold on a national scale, it not only loses its edgy, subversive quality, but it becomes downright reactionary—feeding an antifeminist backlash in a way that it avoids while still underground.

When the next star comes up from the minors, s/he will likely invent an entirely new form of entertainment or reconfigure or combine existing ones with such vigorous originality that it appears new. Whatever the case, there is not a single drag queen in New York who won't have to make some serious adjustments to her current schtick if it's going to play in Peoria. Yes, the world seems ready to receive the drag message. But in a strange way it seems that many drag queens themselves are not ready. There are some hopeful candidates, **The Misstress Formika** comes instantly to mind, perhaps because she seems to have found a way to speak to gay and straight, uptown and down, hip and not-so all at the same time. She is keenly aware of the gulf that exists between gay and straight culture, as well as between women and men, and has chosen to confront it head-on. That may be just the dose of originality required to make the leap to the big time. As a whole, though, the drag queen community seems as surprised as

Bunny: I think she's *very* sexual.

Flloyd: But she's not trashy, talking about dicks and stuff. Not sexual energy.

Hapi Phace: Why is Madonna so popular in the straight world, then? Why can't a gay man dressed as a woman do the same things that a straight person would? Get up and talk about dick and sex and farts. They can't! They, for some reason, have to be polite to make it big.

Flloyd: I think it's harder for a straight person to accept a man dressed as a woman talking about sex. I think it intimidates them. I mean, even *To Wong Foo* . . . had all of the sex stripped right out of it. There was nothing sexual.

Miss Understood: It'll happen sooner with a drag queen than with an out gay man, because an out gay man is too threatening.

any at the sudden exposure it has received. It's almost as if someone switched on the light in a dark and crowded room, catching nearly all of its inhabitants with their pants down—if you will.

Queen Mothers

Stand-up comic Lea Delaria once joked that during a cross-country drive, it occurred to her somewhere around the middle of the country that there were no gays or lesbians in middle America. "It's like," she joked, "God looked down from the heavens and said 'Gay people, move to the sides!' " Many do, of course, choose to escape to the coastal metropolises that have for generations proved relatively safe havens not only for gays, lesbians and assorted gender fugitives, but for all people defined to some extent by their difference. They escape to Los Angeles, to San Francisco or New York—often from brutal rejection from friends and family back home, wherever that may be. For insouciant drag queens, young people whose gayness might not be so easy to hide, it can be even worse. Effeminacy is often viewed as the ultimate crime of the gay man, even more degrading to a family than a daughter's butch appearance. So off they go, by hook or crook, and—following a path as instinctual as the one that leads salmon back home to spawn—they get themselves to New York.

After landing in Oz, it does not take long for newcomers to begin the process of piecing together new families, somewhat less conventional, but often considerably more nurturing, than the ones they left behind. New York is a city of alternative families; it may be one of the unique aspects that makes New York the extraordinary city that it is. (A Southerner once noted that while people from the South are always cordial and polite, they rarely trust another much farther than they can throw one another, whereas

Part VI: Sex and the Single Queen

Julian: Do any of you feel that, in doing drag as much as you do, perhaps you're sacrificing a considerable amount of sex life?

[Laughter.]

Chicklet: No, I take cabs.

Flloyd: You definitely sacrifice something, but I don't know if it's sex life.

Miss Understood: Well, you get come on to a lot by these straight-identified men. I don't call them straight men—

Chicklet: Cabdrivers.

Miss Understood: They *think* they're straight. I don't think anybody has to 'fess up here, but I think there are some people that go ahead and do

New Yorkers, famous for their brusqueness and insularity, are initially slow to open up, but in the long run are exceedingly trusting and familial.)

The Drag Queens of New York are especially effusive about their families. Three queens in particular are alluded to again and again in the stories drag queens tell about arriving here, needing and eventually finding some mother hen to take them under their wing. Each is a unique character, but they all made life, first, livable and, second, worth living for the babies they raised. They are **Marsha P. Johnson, Ethyl Eichelberger** and **International Chrysis**. If the drag world has any saints in heaven, they are this triumverate. From the shiftless street life of working girl Marsha, to the glamorous if somewhat surreal world of Chrysis, to the heady theatrical life of "Queen" Ethyl, their lives exhibit all of the drama, color and strangeness that is drag.

Marsha P. Johnson, as she is always called, was one of the queens at Stonewall. This alone qualifies her for sainthood, as this small band of angry misfits fired the first shot in what eventually became a full-scale revolution. The riot that occurred outside of the Stonewall Inn mid-summer of 1969, and which was fueled in large measure by drag queens like **Marsha P. Johnson** and her longtime friend **Sylvia (Ray) Rivera,** is generally viewed as the Bunker Hill of the gay liberation movement. It does, to a certain extent, remain the subject of some debate, as witnesses, scholars, historians and critics pore over the minutiae of who was where when and who actually gave a damn. Social observers like Fran Lebowitz maintain that the rosy filter of hindsight has caused many to overestimate the importance of the event, that at the time it barely made a ripple. While that may or may not be accurate, history has declared that moment the key that unlocked the door to the anger and indignance of a major political movement.

Marsha P. Johnson was there, as she had been everywhere else. She was the quintessence of the "Street Queen," a breed of indigent, yet

these guys once in a while. But at the same time, you can't—

Flloyd: In drag?

Miss Understood: Some people do. But there are some people who when they're out of drag are still very androgynous, especially recently. And a lot of them wear a little lipstick or whatever. Those queens probably can date those people. A lot of us are not the same people out of drag and we wouldn't date someone like that. And we wouldn't want to date them. And they wouldn't want to date us. We live in different worlds. So in a way, it kind of gets on my nerves after a while because you kind of think, I really need to be meeting people out of drag a little more often. You know? I do. I do date people out of drag. That's really the only people I would go on a date with. I wouldn't dress in drag to go on a date with one of those people. That's for kicks, if I happen to be there.

completely active cross-dresser. The life of the Street Queen could not be further removed from the lives of the current generation of downtown hipsters. **Hattie Hathaway,** who met Marsha in 1974 when he was making his first investigatory sorties to the West Village, remembers her as being "kind of batty." Bearing an odd resemblance to Flip Wilson, as often as not she was on roller skates and managed somehow to change outfits completely during a single ride from one end of the Village to the other. To the naive spectator, she might have appeared to be just another member of the ranks so often referred to as "The Homeless Mentally Ill." A passerby on the street might never have imagined that she was the founding member of S.T.A.R. (Street Transvestite Action Revolutionaries), a self-styled political action group that tried, largely in vain and with literally no money, to build housing and provide services for the growing numbers of young, homeless gay, lesbian and transgendered souls who began arriving in New York during the late sixties.

Marsha P. Johnson, nee Malcom Michaels, Jr., never pined for the typical conventions of home and hearth. By all accounts she was drawn to the street, and was happiest there, turning tricks, dressing up and, of course, taking care of others. She has been described alternately as nutty as a fruitcake and as sane as can be. For a while she was a member of the **Hot Peaches,** a drag theater troupe that continues to tour the nation and the world. She was apparently outspoken and generous to a fault, willing to give up her last cent if she thought it would do some good. All of this can be readily verified by anyone who claims to have known her (**Ethyl Eichelberger** called her Saint Marsha), but always now through a filter of anger and sadness as the circumstances of her death remain unresolved. Her body washed up near the west side piers of the Hudson River in Manhattan several years ago, the result (according to police) of a suicide, either accidental or otherwise. Members of the West Village community fervently

Julian: But you all spend a lot of time in gay clubs where cruising is what happens. A lot of people go to gay clubs to meet other men, to go home and have sex with them. Now, you're there dressed in drag . . . Is that frustrating?

Bunny: No, because we don't want the gays anyway! Honey, you're not gonna waste a shave on a fucking faggot! This is totally different from everyone, but the first time I ever saw drag queens, in Chattanooga, Tennessee, was in a gay club. They were the only people I'd ever seen in my life with false eyelashes, sequined gowns, and long wigs. And I thought, This is so incredible. And I was drawn to them, literally just unable to move. They'd say, "Hey, Baby!"

Flloyd: And you wanna touch 'em. Touch their wigs, and feel their tits, and—

Bunny: Yeah, and I did! No, I thought, They're so beautiful. They're so incredible. But yet, they're at this gay bar, and who is going to want them?

maintain that such an event is simply not possible, given **Marsha P. Johnson's** nature. Furthermore, given her dealings with drug dealers and violent johns, the case for murder could be easily made—if the police were willing to pursue it. The case remains open, although hope has dimmed that the truth will ever be sorted out.

As a twelve-year-old from the Bronx, **International Chrysis** joined the drag scene of the late sixties, entering pageants and stunning audiences with her rare beauty. A dead ringer for quintessential Broadway gypsy Ann Reinking, Chrysis was by her own admission "a wild child," whose chief goal for the majority of her life was "to have a great time." Unlike most pure drag queens, Chrysis had implants that caused her to joke that her breasts were done by "Johnson & Johnson." Drag queen elder statesman **Hapi Phace,** who worked with Chrysis on several occasions, recalls that she "loved being split. She adored having big tits and a big dick. She would joke that her measurements were 34, 26, 9. She was very butch in bed." Chrysis observed that she never went through a complete sex change because then she would be "just another woman." As such, she broke considerable ground, proving that strangeness and glamour could, in fact, coexist—even enhance each other.

By the mid-seventies, Chrysis was a true international celebrity. She had appeared at the Jewel Box Review and Club 82, two major drag reviews that enjoyed widespread public appeal, as well as with the **Hot Peaches,** with whom she toured Europe. She was also a staple of the uptown New York nightlife scene as it was exemplified by Studio 54, the undisputed mother of all nightclubs. There, in the ecstatic whirl of beautiful and famous faces, inestimable wealth and limitless supplies of chemical lubricants, swells mingled with trade, dancing and flitting behind the famous velvet ropes, completely inured to the financial and cultural collapse of the city outside. Chrysis was born to be seen in such a setting and she went

Flloyd: You ended up going home with one.

Bunny: She turned out to be my dad. [Laughter.] No, I thought, Why would gays want to come and see this? Why wouldn't they want to see *men* in their shows? Why do they want to come see these women? Maybe it's because they're in touch with their feminine side. So I think you kind of make a decision when you become known as a drag queen—'cause I mean there's some drag queens that work in drag and look totally different when they're not in drag. They have sex with a gay man and don't let on that they're a drag queen. Hedda complains about how she'll have sex with someone and they'll find out that she's a drag queen and then it will be over. And it seems unfair. But at the same time, what turns you on is what turns you on, and there is nothing that you can do about it except bottle it up and go out and have some Neverland Ranch with llamas and molested children. You know, if you bottle it up, you're going to turn into a worse pervert, so you

over like gangbusters. The director of *The Blue Angel,* in which she had appeared, arranged a meeting between Chrysis and surrealist master Salvador Dali, commencing a legendary relationship that would last seven years, until Dali's death. **International Chrysis,** whose name reflected the turbulent times during which she flourished, became Dali's muse. They were inseparable, her many ambiguities serving as the perfect foil for his inverted and virtuosic renderings of life's odder mysteries.

It is Chrysis's role as adoptive mother, however, that the queens working today recall most affectionately. She was the protector and nurturer for many of today's most vital queens, including **Raven-O** and **Perfidia**. Without the shelter, if not the guidance, she provided, one can only imagine where their like might have ended up. Like **Marsha P. Johnson,** Chrysis was the veteran of a difficult childhood—her parents had locked her up in Bellevue before she turned thirteen. She became the mother she never had, in effect, turning her own sense of alienation into the salvation of the many similarly disaffected runaways and orphans who still flock to the streets of New York.

Born James Roy Eichelberger, **Ethyl Eichelberger** left behind a legacy more professional in nature than her two colleagues'. A disciple of, among others, **Charles Ludlam,** and a sometimes contributing member to his Ridiculous Theater Company, Ethyl combined explosive originality with extraordinary stores of talent to tear wide open the theatrical landscape for drag performers. She worked extensively with other companies, including the aforementioned **Hot Peaches,** but it was as a solo performer that she impressed so many. Combining the bravura stage worthiness of her mentor **Charles Ludlam** with a literary inventiveness largely her own, she thrilled audiences with virtuosic star turns in which she recited her own twisted amalgams of stories from antiquity and the day's head-

have to express what turns you on. And gay men, they don't want someone with the trappings of a woman, and they want someone that's manly. And even if the sex between them when they're out of drag is fantastic, to see the person that they're trying to identify with as their lover— which they want to be a *man*—prissing around in high heels, and camping it up in a dress and having such an affinity for women's things, it is a turnoff. And there's nothing that you can do about it.

Hapi Phace: I think there is some truth in what Bunny's saying. I think that Miss Understood made a good distinction about straight-identified guys. The guys that I have sex with are straight identified, in that they have wives, and they live a straight life, and the drag queen thing doesn't freak them out. They're familiar with women. They want to have sex with a man, and they're so bottled up, they're desperate. They'll even have it with *me*. Or bisexual guys it doesn't freak out.

lines, played her trademark accordion and cavorted with the audience—all the while switching costumes and cartwheeling in heels.

"She had an obit in the *Times*" is typical of how those who loved her emphasize her greatness. Surely, they imply, if someone in her line of work made it into "The Paper of Record" then she must have been important. More to the point, though, is that everyone who ever saw her perform—ever—will corroborate her greatness. "She was the first drag queen to go-go dance on a bar," says **Hapi Phace,** who got his start working as her soda 'n' juice girl at the Pyramid. "She was the first drag queen to make a serious impact on theater and performance art," observes **Lady L,** a part-time drag queen who has been keenly observing the scene for years. "Yes, there were drag queens who did serious things and who were interesting. But she was really the first to write all of her own material, perform it and have people sit up and take notice. She was clearly a genius." In point of fact, her obituary in the *Times,* dated August 14, 1990, and written by *Times* theater critic Mel Gussow, noted that Ethyl had been a "flamboyant presence on the New York theatrical scene for the last 15 years as an actor, performance artist, clown and playwright." Gussow went on to note that Eichelberger displayed "the versatility of a circus artist" and that "the classics were never the same once [he] offered his interpretation." The fact that Ethyl had also appeared on Broadway and in movies was not lost on Gussow, who clearly felt the passing of a true New York original. *The Village Voice,* perhaps more akin to Eichelberger than the *Times,* noted that "when he played the Great Women of History, he proved that transcendent drag is really art about art." *Voice* theater critic Michael Feingold wrote that she was "the transvestite as deconstructor, trashing definable gender roles, along with dramatic structure, stage propriety and coherence, while in the very act of asserting them."

Miss Understood: But you see, I think there's so much in between. And I've learned from being a drag queen, because a lot of these guys, they pick you up in drag, they want you to fuck them up the ass, but they say they're *straight.* Now, a lot of them are turned on by the makeup, but then again, makeup is *fake.* Women weren't born with makeup or hair or nails, so if that weren't invented, what would turn these people on? Would they be into men or women?

Bunny: They're freaks.

Miss Understood: I don't know what they are—

Bunny: The hair and the makeup and the heels, it turns them on, honey.

Miss Understood: But if those things didn't exist, what would they like? Men or women? Those things are social constructions. They didn't always exist.

Perhaps even more important to drag queens than her theatricality, however, was Eichelberger's apparent way with other, less seasoned performers. It was as if she could see into the hearts of men and know instinctively when there was a drag queen hiding inside. She encouraged friends to get into drag and, once they were in it, inspired them to heights of performance they did not seem to know they could reach. She harbored many a refugee, turning lives around in ways large and small, all of which is remembered with tremendous fealty by the Drag Queens of New York.

There were, of course, many other drag queen mothers, looking after their ersatz broods. **Jackie Curtis,** for example, one of Warhol's three drag superstars, is often referred to in similar terms. Certainly there are others who are still living, playing a role that circumstance and history seems to have established as necessary and unavoidable. Doing drag in New York has proven for many to be a rewarding way of life, but it has never been among the easiest. Those who do it are often stuck between a past that was difficult and a future that is uncertain. The Queen Mothers see to it that in between there is at least a bit of joy.

Bunny: I think that maybe if it were more acceptable for these people to be gay, they would be more in touch with their own "it's okay to be with a guy." I'm talking now about men who have sex with *transvestites.* Then those men wouldn't have to be with a guy that hates being a guy, whose genitals are taped up into his asshole, who has undergone all kinds of painful operations that he may well die from, that hates his manliness. They want one that's totally passable to fuck them up the ass. That's what they *really* want. They want a beautiful chick with big boobs to pull out a big ol' dick and fuck 'em and make 'em put on their panties to humiliate them. So it's all a shame thing.

Hapi Phace: Chrysis always said that they just want to feel that big dick up their ass while those titties are on their back. 'Cause in their mind they're having sex with a woman, but it's homosexual sex, which is what they want! They want gay sex.

Miss Understood: They're all different, 'cause I

Icon Explanations

The profiles in this field guide are each accompanied by a set of icons, designed to provide at-a-glance information about places in which the queens work (Habitat) and what sorts of work they do (Modus Operandi). Some caveats: rarely does any queen restrict her work to only one category. The lines that divide a Club Queen from a Cable Queen, for example, are visible, yes, but few queens *never* cross them. On the contrary, these are just the sorts of divisions that are meant to be crossed. (After all, that's what cross-dressers do.) There is, in fact, something perverse about exerting this kind of hermetic pressure on drag queens; they have built lives specifically around *not* being limited to one sector or another. It should come as no surprise, then, that a spectator's effort to cloister them within discrete, digestible categories should get thwarted so often. In the face of the Drag Queens of New York, such perimeters become thresholds, opportunities to wreak havoc, a made-up set of circumscriptions just begging to be breached. To get an experienced queen to fit within the strict confines of a rubric (the creation of which she had nothing to do with) is a joyfully fruitless exercise. Where the borders

know this one guy who—there are some—this girl I know—this drag queen I know met this one guy that was completely not into seeing a penis at all, only wanted oral sex. Yet he really liked drag queens. Even though he liked women. He wasn't like "Okay, there's no women around, I'll take a drag queen." He liked knowing that it was a man but not *seeing* that it was a man, which is weird.

Hapi Phace: So what did you say to him?

Miss Understood: I said, "Mister, get out."

Bunny: There's always different degrees of not being able to come to terms with the fact that they want to be with a man.

Miss Understood: There's just a natural variation in the way people are. If you look at men and what's called "masculine": a big hairy man—and then at a little skinny, girlie boy like Kibuki. A lot of people are born that way, like Kibuki, and they feel like "My hormones are unbalanced. I should have been a girl." It's natur-

between the categories do get transgressed, how often and to what end, differs, of course, from person to person.

Why, then, given their evanescence, even attempt to set up a group of categories? Why risk reducing these gals to mere instances of a pattern? The icons are guideposts, really—a simple way of defining the basic topography of the drag performers' landscape. For while there is plenty of fence hopping going on out there, queens tend to make a home base out of one province or another, and barring that, their inclinations do lean toward one direction or another. **Girlina,** for example—the consummate club performer—a gal who clearly rejoices in the intimate shock that her surgical-style lip-sync creates among a barroom full of rapt spectators, is likely never to be found behind an editing table, slogging through hours of videotape, piecing together the various elements of a variety show for the public access channels of cable television. **Chicklet,** however, could be. Likewise, **Charles Busch,** a genuine star of the American theater, will never be seen on a Saturday night hosting a dance party at one of the vast, million-man discos that hug Manhattan's postapocalyptic West Side Highway. **Miss Understood,** of course, will . . . Count on it.

Furthermore, regarding their M.O.'s, some queens, for example, never sing a note; they lip-sync only. Others wouldn't dream of mouthing the words to a recorded performance even if they could sing. Still others do both, happily Hegelian in their flexibility, handily reaping the benefits of both forms. One queen will get her sea legs as a dancer and then move on to stand-up comedy when the spirit moves her. Another spends years toiling in the trenches of the downtown bar scene, only to discover that her true calling is in spinning records in a rock-and-roll saloon.

Flexibility is a valuable asset in the realm of the queen. The scene is restless and turbulent. A girl is wise to bone up on a number of skills and tailor them to a number of venues, as one never knows when the limelight

---

al. There's just as many big, hairy men as little skinny, hairless boys. And there are men that like those kind of boys. And I think those kind of men do grow up thinking they're straight because they like what we call "femininity." But it's not femininity. It's just that women happen to have it more often than men.

Bunny: There are very few of those kind of guys, I think—the kind of guys that like extremely androgynous, pretty boys.

Miss Understood: Those pretty boys are getting hit on all the time. But those men always consider themselves straight.

Bunny: But there are very, very few guys that like pretty boys who are feminine.

Flloyd: I think a lot of what Bunny says is true, but I think that there's also a lot of guys that aren't like that. Because I've gone out with guys who can deal with the fact that I'm a drag queen just fine. It's no problem to them, and

will shift and today's hot spot becomes tomorrow's empty hulk of an edifice. Nevertheless, the M.O. icons do represent a reasonable list of the sorts of specialties practiced by most queens in most settings. Many of them tend to stick with what they are good at, and where that is the case it has been noted. Counting chickens, though, is discouraged. Taking note of the dynamic push and pull of life in the drag jungle is a better idea.

Habitat Icons

Club Queens

The great majority of drag queens have spent a significant amount of time working in clubs. It is the unavoidable venue in which the journeyman phase of a queen's development gets played out. It is a relatively safe arena in which to hone one's look and drag personality. There are more jobs with more money available to performers in clubs than in other venues, and the money is relatively good. Queens' names are included in the clubs' advertising, and for promoters, popular queens can mean a substantial boost to revenue.

There are a growing number of establishments in which queens are expected to perform at some point during the night, but those gigs are jealously guarded by the few who have them. And who could blame them? A running gig in a popular bar means good money, faithful customers and a regular opportunity to work up fresh material and do what queens most love to do. These performances, most of which occur at hours during which mere mortals are well into REM sleep, range from lip-syncing a number or two in a dimly lit corner, to mounting fully staged extravaganzas, entire mini-musi-

they can see that it's just an act and that I don't fetishize it.

Miss Understood: You mean gay guys?

Flloyd: Gay guys.

Bunny: Yeah, but that's because nobody can take a fist like you.

Miss Understood: Bunny, do you mean that there aren't that many gay men that call themselves gay?

Flloyd: I think there are a lot of people who can just accept the fact that it's your career, and just deal with it rationally.

Miss Understood: Like Kibuki walking down the streets of New York is a boy all the time.

Bunny: *Those* are not men that think of themselves as gay.

Miss Understood: That's what I'm saying.

Bunny: I'm talking about the people in Champs [a

cals or farces which often employ other performers to flesh out the cast. If a girl can strike a chord among the patrons of a given club or bar, then she might be looking at months, even years, of steady employment.

Working in the clubs is, however, a devil's bargain. While the availability of these jobs has enabled many queens to make a living doing drag, in many cases they are expected merely to show up and decorate the space. Over the long term, this can have a decidedly numbing effect; for people who love nothing more than to dress up and perform, to be asked simply to stand around and make nice with the patrons is like opening up the prison gates and asking Willie Horton to just stay put. However, the recent rise of the "monster clubs" in New York has meant an abundance of work for those queens willing to mill about adding visual excitement to the often dehumanizing scale of the clubs that continue to open under the relentless auspices of Peter Gatien, the Godzilla of New York nightlife. Posing the same sort of threat to smaller, neighborhood bars that, say, Barnes and Noble Superstores pose to independent booksellers, these massive motion machines attract literally thousands of eager, gonad-bearing revelers to a seemingly endless succession of loud, often drug-driven disco extravaganzas. Queens are a natural addition to these nightly carnivals, adding to the tireless Mardi Gras atmosphere and helping, at least, to offset the almost fascist ethos of countless identical, hyper-male torsos, mechanical music and the heartless sexualization of every object in sight. More than a few queens have speculated that it is the very oppressiveness of so many "muscle queens" that precipitated the need for some sort of feminized antidote within the world of New York nightlife. These prototypical gym-perfect bodies, of which there are so many and which are warehoused in the gay enclave that is the New Chelsea, have been compared to the infamous clones of the West Village seventies.

So, while it is good to see a lucrative job market open to a relatively

bar in Chelsea]. The number of people in Champs that would be after a pretty, feminine boy . . . All of them would prefer a muscle man.

Julian: But they've all moved together into the same neighborhood anyway. They've all sort of solved that problem by ghettoizing themselves.

Miss Understood: I think those men who like pretty boys all grew up thinking they're straight. They're all wrapped up in thinking they're straight, even though they're really not.

Those guys do exist, but it's hard to even date them because they're so uptight and screwed up. *They're* the ones that are really screwed up. They're the ones I think would be gay or bi if there weren't all these trappings around them.

Chicklet: I'm sorry, but don't no faggot want no skinny faggot bitch. That is my experience. No muscle boy wants a queeny, faggy bitch roaming around the house in slippers. I'm sorry.

large number of queens, it is also disheartening to see the likes of, say, **Linda Simpson,** once the unequaled doyenne of quirky, energetic, drag-infused East Village theatricals, devoting her energy to working for the drag equivalent of IBM. The trade-off is readily apparent, and even Linda herself will say that those gigs have a Stepford-izing effect on most queens. "It's like a slave mentality," she insists. "No one is being rewarded for using their imaginations in that setting, but work is work." Like a rapacious real estate developer who degrades the value of a beautiful stretch of coastline by building on it, thereby cutting off his nose to spite his face, Gatien and his minions might well be flirting with a diminished return if they continue to hire drag performers without finding ways to cultivate what makes them exciting in the first place.

It would be unfair, however, not to note that many of the smaller club owners strive to utilize the unique qualities that are the essence of drag. The redoubtable promoters behind *Jackie 60,* for example—a long-running circus in the shadows of the meat packing district—have taken up the gauntlet with notable zeal and have succeeded in sustaining a weekly festival of drag performances, many of them well thought out and vigorously promoted. Luckily, in even the dullest of nightclub settings, most queens choose wisely not to bite the hand that feeds them, yet can be counted on to transform their environment rather than vice-versa.

Theater Queens

The theater has historically been the one guaranteed refuge of the drag queen. In productions that range from fully enfranchised, "legit" stagings of the classics to the most bizarre, outlaw mountings of obscure works by unknown authors, the theater has been the one great, all-encompassing rubric under which drag and cross-dressing could exist, essentially free

Flloyd: There's other things besides muscle boys, though.

Julian: Is that what interests you?

Chicklet: I don't think it interests me. I don't find it interesting.

Flloyd: Linda thinks you're hot.

Chicklet: I think Linda's hot. But you know—

Julian: Do drag queens ever sleep with drag queens?

[Pause. Laughter.]

Miss Understood: A little bit.

Hapi Phace: It's what's known in the trade as "kai-kai."

Julian: How do you spell that?

Hapi Phace: K-I-K-I.

from the admonitions of society at large. There have even been periods when great practitioners of theatrical or vaudeville-style drag have been openly and enthusiastically celebrated. Certainly, the history of the theater has, until the last century really, been the story of male performers standing for/as their female counterparts. As women began more regularly to play female roles, cross-dressed performance became the exception, no longer the rule, and now, of course, women virtually always play these roles. Men who play female roles in the theater, and occasionally on film, have had increasingly to create their own theatrical space, which, until recently, has been a liminal one. In recent times it has been a space inhabited principally by the likes of vaudeville star **Julian Eltinge; Minette,** a retired star of a national circuit of drag theaters; **John Vaccaro** and the late **Charles**

bell hooks
Author, Professor

I think part of the emphasis in our culture on drag right now is very reactionary—very much about sort of reinscribing a certain kind of femininity that feminism has critiqued, you know? The sort of subversive and transgressive images of drag are being completely undermined by co-optation as a kind of expression of hetero-sexism. I think that when drag was its own particular sub-culture—even within gay culture—it had much more subversive and transgressive potential.

Let's face it, let's talk about money. There [used to be] no money in drag. The key to the way this culture co-opts things radical is usually through commodification. What is ironic to me is that someone like RuPaul who gets brought to us by mass media, marketed to us as "radical," is actually an expression of the power of the conservative standpoint to co-opt and repossess. It's like repossessing a car or something. They can repossess transgressive images in ways that undermine their transgressive potential . . . Lately I've just been having to stress to people how much I believe in interlocking systems of domination, because it's so clear that people who are marginalized on one front can be bought off on another front. And if we don't understand how these things interlock, then we can't see how that process takes place.

It's also that I think it's really hard for people to see how drag is being used against women, particularly against feminist women. It's like "Oh well, bitches, if you don't conform to this, this sort of patriarchally defined femininity, we can find some men who can conform to it, you know? . . . At its best, drag really is a form of radical play that can test the boundaries of gender. But I think when it's enshrined not as a form of play but as a destiny, then it becomes very problematic.

Flloyd: I think it's K-A-I, isn't it?

Bunny: It's Q-I-Y-E-A.

Hapi Phace: It comes from the lesbian vernacular from years ago, and it means two butches or two femmes sleeping together.

Bunny: I think it's a relative of Kiki. [Laughter.]

Miss Understood: If I liked a guy and he was also a drag queen, but I liked him as a guy—

Hapi Phace: But there is sort of a taboo on the practice. Whoops! I used that term.

Bunny: The drag craze has just started. Maybe now drag queens will slowly begin to be thought of as prizes. "As the shamans were treasured among the Indian tribes, the Berdash were reserved for the most victorious warriors." But you know, I think that one problem is that gays are so status conscious—the

Ludlam of Ridiculous fame; as well as members of Warhol's coterie. Currently, the major drag stars working with the theatrical milieu include **Everett Quinton,** who carries the flame of the Ridiculous Theatrical Company; author, playwright and performer **Charles Busch;** pastiche artist, diva and hypochondriac **Lypsinka** and the members of the various independent companies such as La Grande Scena Opera, Theatre Couture and the Black Lips Performance Cult.

A minority of personalities profiled in this volume could be considered Theater Queens. *The Drag Queens of New York*'s goal is to look at and define the recent rise of drag above and beyond its traditional circumscription within, at best, the very fringe of "legitimate" Lincoln Center–style culture. In other words, since drag in the theater is neither new nor radical, it doesn't really figure into the dynamic and far-reaching impact of drag seen recently throughout popular culture.

A recent offshoot of theatrical drag is nightclub drag, which for all intents and purposes comes under the category of Theater. As lip-syncing has increasingly lost favor, more and more queens with legitimate vocal talent have been setting up shop in cabarets and nightclubs. Even though many of these performers began in the bars/clubs, the essence of their current work (singing accompanied by live musicians, dancing, comedy routines etc.) must be viewed as within a theatrical milieu. True, there will be occasions when the line between a nightclub performance and a club performance per se is virtually undetectable, but that way lies madness.

Cable Queens

The advent of public access on the New York cable networks provided a wide-open forum in which all manner of unconventional programming

mainstream gays. Because they've been looked down on all their life, they've got to have that Izod, they've got to have that credit card—

Miss Understood: That Chelsea boy . . .

Hapi Phace: A trophy . . .

Bunny: And a drag queen is a stigma kind of thing, because they're looking for someone they can show off. Plus gays are so shallow in rela-tionships. They have a boyfriend, they're in love, then they're out in a goddamn club showing him off, trying to get a little bit more excited when they fuck him later on because everyone's been slobbering over him. Please, if I have a man, I'm taking care of him. I'm not flitting around a goddamn club with him. [Belches and gets ready to leave.] Honey, I'm sorry. Even in drag I'd take care of him. But out of drag, I get so excited I could just squirt a load of AIDS-riddled come out of my three-inch hor-

could be foisted upon an unwitting audience. Initially the availability of time slots made local legends out of regular citizens who were willing to make spectacles of themselves. Rare is the New Yorker who isn't intimate with Robin Byrd, the macramé-clad exhibitionist who has arguably brought the lowest kind of pornography to the eager citizens of Manhattan. Blowing the lid off what was considered acceptable programming, Byrd (whose mantra "Settle back with your loved one, and remember, if you don't have a loved one, you always have me!" has been drummed into the consciousnesses of a whole generation of local viewers) forged a new ring into which freaks and miscreants of all sorts were able to throw their hats and make an impression. It represented a democratic explosion of creative, political and sexual energy by the people and supposedly for the people.

The televised equivalent of cheaply produced 'zines (the hastily assembled, Xeroxed limited-edition magazines that individuals produce at personal expense), the shows that regularly appear on public access are for the most part crude and fetishistic. Dog lovers and pupeteers, Jews for Jesus and nightclub denizens, transgendered crypto-sadists and the eunuchs who love them, cabaret artists and experimental videographers, new age prophets and old age hookers—these are but a few of the archetypes who mix age-old showmanship with twenty-first-century modes of electronic distribution to comprise the low-rent firmament that is New York's public access cable television.

Into this Dante-esque ether strode the Drag Queens of New York. Given the profane intensity of many of the programs already on the air by the time they arrived, queens found themselves in the novel position of presenting relatively tame entertainment in public access terms. Who can know to what extent these broadcasts have played a role in the ascendancy of drag? Perhaps untold numbers of domestic or uptown types who would have never seen a drag queen sashaying across Fourteenth Street

---

mone-shriveled cheesy-foreskin wrapped-up penis and pop my shit- and piss-filled diapers—and halla-fuckin'-looya!

[Bunny exits. Big pause.]

Miss Understood: So what do you think of Bunny's dress?

Chicklet: I loved it.

Flloyd: I love it every time she does that.

Chicklet: When she said, "squirt out her cheesy..." Oh, that was fierce.

Miss Understood: What was going on with her breath? I think she was drinking before she came here.

Linda Simpson: But the thing is, I think modern youth is becoming a little more open. Like a lot of those kids at Limelight on Wednesday night are kind of like drag queens.

(let alone in performance), were thrust into face-to-face encounters that challenged their notions of what drag has to offer. Or perhaps not. Either way, the otherness that queens have always represented may have at least been worn down by years of exposure within the dark nether regions of cable television.

The impact of drag programming on cable TV cannot be overstated, if only in terms of exposing the full extent to which the media transmits an increasingly gay sensibility. After decades of laboring under the illusion that drag queens have been emulating stylish and voguish women, citizens at large have had to witness that the case is in fact reversed; much of style and voguishness is the product of gay sensibilities, not the other way around.

Sandra Bernhard
Author, Actress, Comedian

One of the biggest problems I have with drag queens is that I think there's an innate kind of anger toward women. Not on all of their parts. But on some of their parts. That they're not, that they aren't actually women. And I think that they get attracted to women who are bigger than life and not very viable as female creatures. I think that the women . . . that they cling to, the over-the-top, bigger-than-life [women are] not really a fair reflection or a complete reflection of what [being] a woman is about.

I think that it's interesting, and it's funny, and it's entertaining, but I think it's gone to another level now where it's almost replacing an accurate look into what a woman feels and thinks. And women are in a precarious kind of position right now in terms of having a lot of their rights taken away . . . So I think, I don't know, I have mixed feelings about drag queens. I think that they take away a certain amount of reality that women need to have right now.

Impresarios

This category is reserved for those few queens, and occasional civilians, who have devoted themselves to the introduction, development and upkeep of other queens' careers. This uncharacteristic altruism can occur on several levels and in as many venues. From the enormity of **The**

Hapi Phace: The only gay boyfriends I've had in the last ten years are twelve years younger than me, 'cause to them it's not a big deal.

Flloyd: 'Cause all the people of your generation have died.

Hapi Phace: Well, that is true.

Linda Simpson: Flloyd, that isn't funny!

Flloyd: I'm sorry. I forgot you were in the room.

Miss Understood: She forgot that you were on your deathbed.

Hapi Phace: Well, Linda, you never had gay sex *until* you got into drag.

Flloyd: Linda wouldn't have sex if it weren't for cabdrivers.

Linda Simpson: It's very easy, if you want, dressed in drag—I find—to have sex. Even with hot guys. It's easy. You know what I mean? It

"**Lady**" **Bunny**'s yearly extravaganza *Wigstock,* to **Mona Foot**'s on again, off again *Star Search,* these queens expend inordinate amounts of time, energy and even personal expense to provide a setting in which new performers, anxious for a shot at the big time, can cut their teeth and eventually gain stardom. In a society in which there are no schools, no apprenticeships and no master classes in which drag tyros can experiment and take risks in relative safety, the importance of the spaces provided by these visionaries to the growth of the drag industry cannot be overestimated.

The demise of the Boy Bar and the Pyramid as drag venues has meant a sharp drop in the number of functioning impresarios, highlighting the extent to which even the most industrious of drag queen promoters rely on the availability of space, audience and publicity. Many queens, impresarios and otherwise, have voiced their desire to find new spaces in which to present new performers. However, bars that feature sufficient theatrical space are rare, as are theatrical spaces that can double as watering holes. The confluence of the two elements is essential, it seems, to creating the atmosphere in which queens can be seen in the best possible light.

Some intrepid souls are seeking out spaces in altogether new places, cabarets and nightclubs among them. If drag is to continue to expand its audience and enter the mainstream in earnest, then its stars will have to find their way out of the bars and discos that comprise their primary stages. Reaching the widest possible audience will mean playing on a popular field, in settings that don't scare the living daylights out of average Americans. It may be up to the impresarios to make this leap, thereby shifting the very nature of the category from giving new queens a place to grow to bringing drag to stages where it previously has never played.

---

might be a fleeting thing, a *really* fleeting thing. But it's, like, *cute* guys. And the thing is, it becomes kind of addictive, because you think, This hunk—I could never have him as a guy, which is probably true.

Flloyd: Les, you could never have this guy.

Linda Simpson: Well, that's what I have to say.

Hapi Phace: Well, are these guys gay or straight? Are they interested in a relationship or just sex?

Linda Simpson: They would probably identify themselves as straight. It's a sex thing. It's a fantasy. I'm a fantasy woman for them for the night.

Flloyd: But that fucks with my head too much.

Linda Simpson: Tell me about it! I put myself through it!

Modus Operandi Icons

Lip-sync

Who can pinpoint a time when mouthing the words to recorded performances became an accepted convention among drag queens? No one. Yet at some point, the age-old tradition of singing live, either with a band or over prerecorded instrumentals, was infringed upon by this oddly disembodied technique. For a culture steeped in the ethos of opera divas and operatic singing stars such as Streisand, Garland and Midler, lip-sync presented both a problem and a solution. For professional chameleons like **Jim Baily**, who combine visual and vocal endowments to create uncanny impressions of half a dozen legendary women in one evening, lip-syncing could only have chipped away at their audience. But for queens who had always had the enthusiasm but not the technical wherewithal to pull off such a tour de force, the rise of lip-syncing must have proven a truly exhilarating possibility.

The advent of low-cost high fidelity has led to the technological democratization of the voices of great singers. Almost overnight, mere shower singers became Evelyn Champagne Kings or Shirley Basseys, while true vocal artists were stripped of their unique power to embody the likenesses of those same stars. Perhaps this explains the lingering disdain that many queens have for lip-syncing. It's not hard to understand the elitism that has emerged around this issue from a population whose members view themselves as divinely ordained to protect and sanctify the miracle of great female voices.

Nevertheless, lip-syncing has flourished in the last thirty years, the chagrin of its detractors not withstanding. The members of the Boy Bar Beauties, for example, were forbidden to do anything else. The appeal is

Flloyd: I don't want to have someone in my house that's not going to talk to me.

Linda Simpson: They'll talk.

Flloyd: The next day, when I'm in drag.

Linda Simpson: I feel like I'm a sex therapist. I just don't get paid for it, you know?

Chicklet: You get paid.

Hapi Phace: One time I met this guy at the bar and he goes, "Wow, you're the only man in here that's really butch and masculine." You know, and I have to say, "Well, I'm not what you think I am." But he kept on and on and on until he insisted on coming home with me—going on about how I was the only "manly man" in the whole bar.

Miss Understood: You?

Hapi Phace: Shut up, Grandma's talking. I don't have much longer left in this world. And then we get to my house, and we have sex. That was like

clear. Few of even the best singing queens can whip up the kind of high-octane fire that, say, Barbra or Liza can—not to mention provide the vast and impressive orchestrations featured on their albums. And given gay culture's deep ties to music and great singers, a talented lip-sync artist working with the right tune in the proper setting is at a considerable advantage in many ways. Anyone who already knows the ecstasy that accompanies, say, the rare concert version of Gloria Gaynor's "I Will Survive" can only be moved to euphoria to see it brought to life by lip-sync titan **Princess Diandra**. Mouthing each utterance, each breath with astonishing accuracy, exposing aural details that the unaided ear might not catch, suggesting visuals that enlarge and dramatize the vocal performance, Diandra's craftsmanship exemplifies precisely what high-quality lip-sync has the potential to do: make a great vocal performance even greater. In living out the drama of a song the musical depths of which have already been plumbed by the recorded vocalist, the drag queen makes a recording more interesting, more meaningful and more immediate—not to mention funnier and more fabulous.

In the best instances, both singer and lip-syncer benefit from this decidedly post-modern symbiosis. The hint of vampirism at the heart of lip-sync provides a bonus frisson that only heightens the voyeuristic thrill. There is a morbid exchange between the voiceless queen and the disembodied vocalist: without the other each is stuck in sort of techno-limbo. A recorded performance is a quasi-lifeless facsimile of a quivering throat in the dark of a recording studio, a hi-fi version of the undead; it needs a conduit through which to contact the living, a vessel through which to reach the ear with maximum impact. Likewise, the mum performer, like a dreamer stuck in a nightmare in which she opens her mouth but cannot scream, reaches for the stereo with polished talons, wraps her mouth around the memory of a song and for a few precious musical moments rescues herself

a Saturday night and so the next night I had to go to work at the Pyramid and do my show. And I'm sitting there at the bar, and Hattie's sitting there, out of drag—I'm in drag, getting ready to go on—and this guy walks in the door of the Pyramid! He gets up to me, goes, "Oh my God!" turns on his heels, and runs out the door! So, I say to Hattie—later, *onstage*—she gets into drag a few minutes later—and I'm onstage and I go, "Hattie, did you ever meet a guy who told you you were really butch and the most manly man he had ever met, and you go home and you have sex with him, and the next day you're sitting at the bar getting ready for your drag show, and he walks in the door, takes one look at you and goes, 'Oh my God!' and runs out the door?" And Hattie goes, "No, Hapi." Two weeks later, Hattie called me like three days before a show and she says, "I want to talk to you about something but *onstage*." So we get onstage, and she goes, "Hapi, remember when you asked . . ." and she recounted my whole story. Then she says, "Well, that's never

from the abyss of silence. The effect of the synthesis of the earthbound, aphasic queen and the soaring, disembodied voice of the diva can be disorienting but not unfamiliar to certain listeners.

To a generation raised on music videos, the suspension of disbelief required by a lip-sync performance is considerably less difficult to achieve. After all, what are music videos if not lavishly contrived lip-synced performances? Decades of movie musicals have employed lip-syncing to achieve their effects. Film and television, such as they are, require extensive looping and lip-syncing to finish the illusion that will ultimately impact an audience. So it is for those drag queens who lip-sync.

For purists who maintain that lip-syncing is merely glorified ventriloquism, an inverse puppet show incapable of providing the excitement of a live vocal performance, the argument can be made that there is ample fuel for merriment in the uniquely infernal challenge that lip-syncing presents. These artists are the funambulists of the drag world, forced by the unyielding authority of the recorded performance to walk a very fine, often shaky line. The existential quality of having to adapt to and maintain the tempo and tenor of a prerecorded performance can be lost on no one familiar with Samuel Beckett or Fritz Lang. It is the theatrical equivalent of George Jetson's dog-walking treadmill: automatic, inexorable and thoroughly modern. An undeniable part of the thrill of watching lip-sync is the subtextual, morbid wish that the artist will screw up, miss a word or skip to the wrong verse. To increase that sense of macabre anticipation, certain performers, the true Evel Knievels of the trade, like to stretch the odds on purpose. **Lypsinka,** for example, has made a career out of editing together insanely complicated audio montages which include spoken as well as musical passages. After what must be mindnumbing hours of transliteration and memorization, in which she becomes almost one with the machine, she presents a fully mounted the-

happened to me. But, did you ever meet a guy in the street who you picked up who thought you were really butch and you went home and had sex with him, and the next morning you were at breakfast and he tells you a story about how he saw this guy at the bar and thought he was really butch—"

Linda Simpson: He had done the same thing to Hattie? He had slept with Hattie after he had slept with you?

Hapi Phace: Right, right. The same guy. Hattie picked the same guy up on the street, and the guy at breakfast goes through this whole story of meeting a guy and walking into the club and seeing this queen and going, "Oh my God" and gunning out the door because he *forgot to buy a bottle of water.* And then he comes back in the club and the queen is up on the stage telling that story, which he had heard—the whole story. And the guys goes, "Yeah, and he was up there with this *other* queen, this really *ugly* drag queen. *He*

atrical tour de force in which she mouths the entire ninety-minute spectacle, much of which flies at a manic pace, without missing a single beat.

For those who do screw it up, there is ample fodder for comedic brinkmanship. Few things please an audience more than a queen who turns a momentary lapse into a well-timed comic gesture, rescuing herself—as all great comedians must—from the jaws of ignominy and glorifying herself in the process. (Watch especially how the quickest queens incorporate the undignified task of grabbing tips from fans into the rhythms and poetry of a song.) For those who make it through a performance without a hitch, there are the sorts of accolades reserved for downhill skiers, championship ice-skaters or, perhaps more appropriately, synchronized swimmers.

Finally, in the midst of all this interpretive athleticism, the lip-syncing drag queen also reaps the pleasures of being both performer and audience member. Anyone who has ever danced around the living room, singing along to his or her favorite song, knows the dual joy of listening to and cavorting with the artist on the recording. When a queen is working a song she truly loves, it shows. The visual performance is simultaneously inspired by the audio; her devotion as a fan is apparent in the intensity with which she listens while she works. There is a touch of Fred and Ginger in the partnering of lips and voice—complete with all the romance, glamour and tension that such partnerships engender. One can only speculate about how the Lizas, Bettes and Judys might feel about providing the voices for countless mugging drag queens. As Ginger Rogers has been quoted as saying on more than one occasion, "Yeah, but I had to do it backwards and in heels!"

Singing

Some queens do it, some queens don't. Some should and some should not. Given the historically important relationship between the gay listen-

---

looked good in drag. The *other* one looked like a horrible hag. I don't even know what her name was." And Hattie looks at him and goes, "Hattie. That other horrible hag of a queen was me." But the moral of the story is that sometimes, for me, I expect men to freak out.

Flloyd: And he was actually just going to get a bottle of water?

Hapi Phace: He was actually just going to get a bottle of water.

Flloyd: I don't feel like that many men come on to me in drag, but I just feel like I'm intimidating. That's my excuse. Not that I'm ugly. I'm intimidating.

Julian: But your drag is different.

Flloyd: Yeah, I've got blood coming out my mouth.

Miss Understood: The point is, the person that I would get that serious with would have to be some-

ers and divas, who better to realize that relationship than a gay male diva?

There is also of course the small matter of the octave leap. While makeup and creative prostheses can transform even the manliest man into a passable facsimile of a woman—or at least a reasonable fantasia on a feminine theme—even the best male singers face an often insurmountable obstacle in achieving the vocal equivalent of halfway decent drag. The few queens who make a habit of singing live have worked out a solution in developing their falsettos. This soprano-esque pseudo-register can sound like anything from a gorgeous, shimmering tone to a mousy shriek, depending on everything from the queen to the day of the week. The falsetto, however, is to the voice what drag is to the body, and with those who do it well (**Varla Jean Merman** comes instantly to mind) the effect can be both hilarious and harrowing. In the case of **Joey Arias,** on the other hand, a Betty Page look-alike who "channels" the voice of Billie Holiday, science may indeed have no satisfactory explanation or description of what he's doing with his larynx. Perhaps it's better that we don't know. Whatever the technical term, he achieves the uncanny effect of sounding remarkably like Holiday without seeming actually to impersonate her.

Dancer

Relatively few of the queens herein work under the heading of Dancer, but those who do present all sorts of interesting questions. Why are their bodies so feminine? Why does, say, **Candis Cayne** look more like a showgirl than most showgirls do? Where does she pack her penis? Few of the queens who dance have any substantial classical training and those who do show it. **Afrodite,** for example, brings to every performace—even those in which she is standing stock still—an economy of movement, a dancer's

body who'd be so progressive thinking in so many ways that the drag wouldn't faze them at all.

Hapi Phace: Right. Exactly! You know, if I think it'll freak them out and I don't like them, I just invite them to the show rather than break up with them.

Flloyd: The way I do things is so different. I use the name Flloyd because I don't want to have a drag name. I don't want people in the club going "Hey, Susan!" when I'm talking to some cute guy. But,

by the same token, I always tell them immediately—because they always—I always tell them instantly, because I want to get rid of the losers who aren't going to deal with it. I want to scare the people off who can't deal with it. They say, "Oh, what do you do?" I say, "Oh, I'm a drag queen."

Miss Understood: I tell people a lot of the times.

Julian: Chicklet, do you tell people right away?

lines and a profound awareness of her body that are clearly the products of years of conventional, classical training.

There isn't, however, much room in conventional drag settings for dance as we know it. Furthermore, on average, the men who do drag are in no way cut out for the rigors of dance. Not only are their bodies, like most people's, simply not equipped to carry out the back-breaking, knee-splitting work of the dancer, but also the late hours, "casual" nutritional habits and general physical lassitude that are hallmarks of the off-duty drag queen's lifestyle mean that they stand not even a passing chance of pursuing dance in any serious way. Those few queens who are legitimate dancers and who find imaginative ways of fitting the dance into their drag routines treat their bodies altogether differently from the way most others do. Even the members of the New York's world-renowned **Ballet Trocadero**, a troupe of cross-dressed prima ballerinas whose farcical send-ups of the classics are truly hilarious, are all veterans of top-flight dance companies. To see even their most ludicrous parody is to see how intimate they are with the almost monkish lifestyle and Zen-like devotion to their craft that are the sine qua non of the dancer's life.

When **Candis Cayne** is out Ann Miller-ing Ann Miller, her angular body and showstopping gams beg the question that is often asked, usually by women, about drag queens in general but is always asked about her: "Why can't I have legs like that?" Why indeed? A body like Candis's, or **The Misstress Formika**'s or **Sherri Vine**'s highlights the sense of confusion that is built into the human form. In many regards, a thin woman's body, unadorned, is not as different from a thin man's as we are cautioned always to believe. Add to that the fact that men's legs tend to remain leaner longer relative to women's, despite the fact that thin, shapely legs are considered to be one of the hallmarks of an ideal female body. In other words, once it is properly depilated and wrapped in a strong pair of fish-

Chicklet: I do, and I do that comfortably, because I do not speak with people that I find attractive. No offense to anyone, but I just will not speak to someone that I find attractive.

Miss Understood: You'll be alone for a long time.

Linda Simpson: Why?

Chicklet: I don't want to go there. I just would rather not deal with any issue involving that, so I do not acknowledge them. And I've trained myself not to see them visually.

Linda Simpson: Are you playing hard to get?

Flloyd: Sounds like she's playing impossible to get.

Hapi Phace: Her heart was broken.

Chicklet: I just don't look at people on that level, and I don't speak to people on that level.

nets, even the average man's leg resembles more the ideal female femur than many females' do. Perhaps this explains the powerful historical/cultural imperative to decorate the genders so differently. For the radical proposition lurking just under the surface of the joke that is drag is the suggestion that the binary system of gender roles we know so well is pure conceit, nothing more than the agreed-upon rehearsal and performance of arbitrarily established sex-specific behaviors. When the drag queen rehearses the other gender's role, and pulls it off so convincingly, then s/he raises the possibility of real gender trouble.

Then again, this is probably not what is going through **Afrodite**'s head as she slides achingly slowly into her trademark split, mouthing the words with shimmering lips, never taking her eyes off the audience on the way down. More likely she's thinking about what Candis says is at the very heart of why she looks as she looks and does what she does: "There's nothing better than the feeling of an audience applauding and the sound of it. That's what gets you going. Your adrenaline starts pumping. Most of the time I don't remember what I did onstage, I come off blank."

Disc Jockey

For many people, queens and civilians alike, long before there is a crisis of gender identity there is the shock of musical affiliation. When one is an adolescent, aligning one's self with the proper musical genre is right up there with keeping up with the latest cut of blue jean or being accepted by the resident Heather Cabal. In fact, learning to defend one's musical tastes as often as not proves an important training ground for claiming more crucial differences later. Once a sensitive high-school student has managed to raise and defend a flag of devotion to, say, early Joni Mitchell, coming out of the closet as an artist or drag queen is a

---

Linda Simpson: Are you denying yourself pleasure?

Chicklet: No, my life is full of pleasure.

Miss Understood: She ties her hands behind her back when she goes to bed at night.

Hapi Phace: Are you trying to avoid pain?

Chicklet: No, I'm on a particular track in my life and I will not acknowledge any attraction of any sort until I have at least three Emmys.

Miss Understood: Even when you jerk off?

Chicklet: Which I do not do. I am a very tense person.

Miss Understood: You don't masturbate?

Chicklet: I don't masturbate. I don't smoke. I don't do drugs.

Miss Understood: Wait, when was the last time you masturbated?

piece of cake. If the object of the teenager's affection was ABBA or Cher (when her albums still mattered), then by the time graduation comes around, the student has likely developed a sophisticated system of defenses and counter-offensives that will stand him or her in good stead for years to come—not to mention a life-long devotion to the chosen artist. A few prescient queens started collecting good records long before they began collecting corsets, heels and packages of raw tabbouleh. If they were smart, they kept them.

Different tastes lead, of course, to different collections, but the change-ability of the nightlife scene dictates that today's collection of tired disco albums is tomorrow's hot ticket, packing them in at filthy East Village dives and sprawling Chelsea techno-palaces alike. For club and bar owners the advantages of hiring drag queen DJs are clear, and they are hired practically every time a style-mongerer with money needs a supply of something current to push. (Who knows why men in silly frocks are so frequently blessed with the marketable ability not only to sense the elusive pulse of the zeitgeist, but, as often as not, to predict it.) Owners and promoters will always have to hire a jockey to supply a backbeat for whatever the revel, but in hiring a drag queen with a pre-screened collection of the hippest tunes, they get a complete package for a fraction of the cost. Style, sophistication and lots of happy-hostess pheromones ensure that the kiddies stay thirsty on the dance floor.

As it is across all commercial markets, the diversified portfolio is the safest investment, so those queens who possess a strong library in a variety of genres are in the best shape. What they also need—and this is where the men are separated from the boys—is, number one, enough records to supply at least a couple of nights' worth of tunes in a certain style without repeats and, number two, the supposedly rare skill of being able to mix them. These are the queens who really pull down the bucks. Walk into **Miss Guy**'s apart-

---

Chicklet: Last year.

Miss Understood: Are you serious?

Linda Simpson: Liar.

Chicklet: No, I'm not.

Miss Understood: Oh, that's scary and extraordinary.

Linda Simpson: These interviews turn really sad.

Flloyd: Do you have wet dreams?

Chicklet: No, I never have, and I've always wanted to!

Miss Understood: Wait, doesn't that jism have to go somewhere?

Chicklet: No, it doesn't have to go anywhere. Your body'll just reabsorb it, like any other protein.

Miss Understood: How could you not masturbate?

ment, for example, and you know she'll never go broke. Whether she spins it, sells it or wears it, she's got enough vinyl to last a lifetime.

Writer

Many queens have found that the only way fully to express the breadth and scope of their insights and opinions is to get them down on paper. If drag is essentially a theatrical institution, then all these girls are by default playwrights. The form and quality of their work differ widely in this category, more so than in almost any other. From the half-baked monologues delivered extemporaneously during the judging of an amateur strip contest, to the fully realized, award-winning theatrical productions of **Charles Busch**'s plays, writing is an integral part of the drag queen's art, but never easily pinned down.

Drag has always been primarily a visual medium, one in which the artist need not necessarily say anything at all. But for those who have the wherewithal, the possibilities are endless. **Hedda Lettuce** scripts sketches for her cable show in the spirit of Carol Burnett. The members of **Theatre Couture** and **Black Lips Performance Cult** piece together entire passion plays invoking the legends of antiquity as well as stories from today's headlines. Many queens are columnists and correspondents, while others merely dabble in social criticism; most go for comedy.

For the purposes of this guide, this category is reserved for those queens who clearly make a priority of the written word, or who make a conspicuous effort to be seen specifically as a writer. In the same way that many jazz musicians are anxious to have their improvisations viewed as compositions—in other words, they desire to be called composers—there is a valid argument to be made that every time a queen stands upright

Chicklet: I just don't. I'm just a very, um, disciplined person. I'm sorry. That was a bit, um, dry.

Linda Simpson: So to speak.

Miss Understood: Put that in the book: "Chicklet doesn't masturbate."

Linda Simpson: That'll start the book: " 'I do not masturbate,' says Chicklet, a downtown drag queen."

Flloyd: So many fags are so desperate for love

that the first person that they blow in the back room, they're like, "Here's my number. Let's pick out the china pattern." You know what I mean? They're so desperate for love. I think fags get really confused. They want love, but they think they want sex, and they go out looking for sex when what they really want is love. They're so desperate for that love that they're ready to get married to the first person that they blow.

and talks out loud she's involved in some sort of authorship. It is a point worth debating, but for our purposes the category is assigned to those who put pen to paper in a consistent and meaningful way. Cable Queens, those increasing numbers of drag performers who have taken to the local public access airwaves, are not automatically included. The conception and execution of those shows involve skills closer to collage than to writing.

Actor 🎭

All the world's a stage . . . Queens are just bigger hams. Or, in the case of **The "Lady" Bunny,** just eat more ham. Either way, queens are by definition actors all, but in a larger societal way. The distinction the guide makes is in favor of those queens who work regularly in formal theatrical settings; that is to say in plays or on film, with scripts, creating characters and participating in the narrative arc of a fictive scenario.

Those queens found here, for the most part, came to drag from the theater rather than vice-versa. **Sherry Vine,** for instance, has been pursuing the theater in one way or another since high school. Drag did not become a part of her substantial battery of talents until some time after she devoted herself to Thespis. Given the healthy dose of Sherry that her maker Keith brings to practically every role he plays, it will be interesting to see whether he'll ever be able to return to the non-drag character work that brought him to the theater in the first place.

Likewise, **Charles Busch,** the consummate drag actor and natural reference for a player such as Sherry, has starred for years in wildly successful plays of his own creation—virtually always in drag. His reputation as an actor is irrevocably attached to his cross-dressing. This should not, however, distract from the rich and legitimate theatricality of his writing or

Hapi Phace: A lot of gay people in this city, anyway, will not admit that they're looking for love. I mean, it's like, "I want a relationship but I don't want to get involved." How do you do that? But that's life in this city. They don't want to admit they're vulnerable to another person.

Part VII: Queens on Queens

Miss Understood: I find it interesting that you didn't invite one cunty girl, which seems to be the big trend right now. When I was going to come over here, I expected Misstress and Candis and Girlina to be sitting around in a circle.

Linda Simpson: Oh, sorry we disappointed you.

his acting. However, this is all too often precisely the price paid by gifted actors who work in drag. Whatever their talents, the focus of critical and popular attention is always on the outfits. The debate rages on, for example, regarding how history should view the late drag legend and all-around theatrical virtuoso **Charles Ludlam**. Many observers naturally look at Ludlam as a drag queen first and then as an actor/playwright—even his longtime lover and the current director of the Ridiculous Theatrical Company. To be sure, there can be no denying the depth of his talent or the scope of his influence as a drag performer. On the other hand, he is also viewed as one of the best and most orignal American playwrights of his era, not to mention a source of unlimited, often crude and difficult energy. That debate will not be solved herein.

Actors can be found in productions ranging from raunchy playlets thrown together for performance in between happy hour and two-dollar schnapps specials, in actual theaters with actual production values and increasingly on television and in movies. Several prime-time network series currently film in New York and nothing generates an edgy tone like a drag queen. Producers will often toss a queen into the background of the mise-en-scène as an inexpensive metonymy for all that is dangerous, freakish or kinky about The City; the denizen standing in for the den. An alert viewer can catch some of New York's finest at least a few times a month, often playing themselves, in the various cop, journalism and fashion dramas that get played out on the grand stage that is Manhattan. Breaking new ground and setting new precedents as the first genuine soap opera drag queen, **Christian Womyn,** a low-key starlet rarely seen outside of professional gigs, has been spotted recently on ABC's soap opera *Loving,* as Morgan Fairchild's chess-playing drag queen friend. Whatever.

To Wong Foo, Thanks for Everything, Julie Newmar, the Steven Spiel-

---

Miss Understood: No, I was actually— They intimidate me, actually. I was—

Flloyd: I was surprised that Misstress or Sherry wasn't invited—one of that faction.

Julian: Sherry was invited—

Miss Understood: Fuck Sherry.

Flloyd: Fuck him.

Linda Simpson: Getting shady, ladies?

Hapi Phace: She's in a show tonight. That's why.

Miss Understood: I feel like drag is losing its campy edge in some ways. I'm not putting down what they do, either. I like what all those people do. I like what everyone's doing, but I feel like the kind of thing I'd like to be doing sort of ended by the time I started doing it. You know, like the more twisted and campy kind of humor is being lost.

berg–produced, big-budget family film about drag—the first of its kind—caused tectonic movement in the New York drag community as queens moved heaven and earth for a spot in the film. **Sweetie,** not an actor by trade, ended up the big winner among the horde of eager New York comers. As the only queen with lines who was not played by one of the major, reputedly straight stars, she was the envy of the entire queen scene, supplying further proof that one need not be an actor per se in order to get work most thespians would kill for.

Artist

For the most part, the fine arts play a relatively minor role in the world of drag. Some drag queens are artists and some artists do drag, but given the particular requirements of the two jobs, the twain rarely meet. After all, who in their right mind would risk getting paint on a $500 pair of Vivian Westwood platforms? No one.

Tabboo!, for example, is a legitimate artist with a legitimate career. And while his fanciful, lyrical paintings, which hang in galleries and museums around the world, are signed Tabboo!, they are viewed neither by buyers nor by critics as "drag art" or "the paintings of a drag queen"—a fate not so easily escaped by those queens who want to act, sing or dance. During its heyday, the Pyramid was festooned with **Tabboo!**'s art. Walls, ceilings and floors were his canvas in a rare instance of art imitating drag, or perhaps vice-versa.

For the most part, when drag queens create visual art it has little bearing on the work they do in drag; therefore few of the queens profiled hereafter are listed as Artist. In cases in which that scenario does not hold up and when the man behind the mask is—aside from being a drag queen—primarily an artist, he is listed as such.

Chicklet: I don't think that humor is being lost.

Miss Understood: I don't mean to be putting them down. I don't mean it that way. I don't think what they're doing is boring. I think what they're doing is very funny.

Linda Simpson: Why do you hate Sherry?

Miss Understood: No, I mean, Sherry's really funny, and—

Flloyd: She's a skag!

Miss Understood: Sherry's really talented and everything.

Flloyd: A clown.

Linda Simpson: Sherry's changed a lot, though, because she used to be more aggressive.

Flloyd: Not enough.

Miss Understood: But sometimes I feel like a lot of the drag queens just kind of, like, don't see what I'm doing because I look a little too

Of course, given the extraordinary lengths to which many of the drag queens of New York go to cohere a look and use their bodies as canvases, there is art (if not artfulness) in the work of even the least artistically inclined. Certainly anyone who's seen **Hattie Hathaway** pull bingo numbers or do a reading at *Grey Gardens,* a drag and performance party that she hosts from time to time, knows that she is as qualified to be rejected by the National Endowment for the Arts as any of those infamous artists whose search for funding triggered its recent diminishment. Hattie's drag includes not only putting on a dress, a wig and big black boots, but also creating an all-encompassing gestalt which—like a Pat Buckley party at the Temple of Dendur—reeks of all the decadence and crumbling glamour that a blowout with the leaders of the latter-day Holy Roman Empire should. Now that's art.

Tuck

Tucking is the one art unique to drag. It involves, quite simply, finding a place to hide one's cock and balls. Queens seem to draw an important distinction between those who tuck and those who don't, while at the same time, there is considerable mystery surrounding what that distinction might be. It is a sensitive point, as many queens, oddly, are embarrassed to discuss it openly. In a subculture in which the body and its many less attractive functions are fodder for all types of parody and exploitation, queens actually get flustered when asked whether they conceal their genitals. Even those who clearly do tuck—a task which generally requires jamming the member against the testicles and up between the legs—will lie and say that they don't. It's almost as if tucking represents the only actual threat to the masculinity they tossed aside in the first place. Perhaps there is a fear that tucking suggests that those who bother to are taking it all a bit too seriously. Whatever the controversy, it is a sore subject and one about which many queens prevaricate. Those willing to

"out there." I don't know, don't you ever feel that of people? Your [Flloyd's] look is pretty "out there" too.

Flloyd: How do you mean? You mean unappreciated?

Miss Understood: Yes.

Flloyd: Yes, I do feel that.

Miss Understood: I feel like they don't know what I'm doing. People have said to me, "I

would love to see you in glamorous makeup one day. I would love to see what you look like." First of all, I think my makeup is glamorous. I don't do "normal" makeup. That bores me, I'm not interested. I would never go up to them and go, "Oh, I'd love to see you in harsh fluorescent makeup." They do what they do, they're good at what they do. That's their thing. This is my thing.

Flloyd: I know exactly what you mean, 'cause I

discuss it agree that it depends on that evening's particular outfit or venue. It has little to do with whether they prefer to tuck as a matter of course. Despite the enigmatic nature of this testy ritual, and a general lack of reliable sources, how each queen tackles tucking is noted where appropriate.

The "Glamour" to "Clown" Scale

"Realness" is a problematic notion when applied to drag. Even those queens who strive to attain it aren't really trying to attain "real" realness. They are after a drag-informed *idea* of what realness might be if queens ruled the planet. It is often interchanged with "glamour," which is probably closer to an accurate description of what those queens are chasing. On the other end of the same scale is "clown drag," which—although no less cartoonish really than "glamour" drag—invloves a more commedia dell arte feel. In "clown drag," every aspect of the costume is ballooned and exaggerated to its maximum. Few queens fully embody only one extreme or the other, creating an even more problematic situation for the morphologist in all of us. As **Chicklet** is fond of saying, "I fall right in the middle of glamour and clown drag. I call it 'Clamour.'" And who could argue? There are still others who, as queens seem wont to do, simply do not fit neatly into any taxonomy, or if they do, don't rest in one place for long. Nevertheless, some attempt has been made herein to give a sense of where each queen might fall were the ground more level.

used to live with Ru and he would always say, "Why don't you try to look prettier? You want to look pretty. You're only young once. You should try and look prettier." Which would only make me want to look uglier.

Linda Simpson: You did a good job at it! I mean, looking different.

Flloyd: Thank you, Linda. You should know.

Miss Understood: I just think people don't look close at what I do sometimes. Some people do. People will watch. But some of the other queens don't understand a different perspective.

Flloyd: Your makeup is almost realistic compared to what you used to do.

Miss Understood: Yeah. So I go up and down on some days. I get a little more sick than other days, and I've sort of developed this certain style that I use.

The Lives
of the Saints

*I*n his tireless effort to play Lacan to Joseph Campbell's Freud, Bill Moyers has uncovered (for the uninitiated) the universal story of the Hero Myth. Every culture, they argue in *The Power of Myth,* seems to have its seminal story, its central narrative, which explains the primary transformation that its people must endure in order to be redeemed. Even the casual observer will notice similarities among the life stories of New York drag queens. While the details differ from soul to soul, the overarching drag story is almost always the same. One is tempted to argue, therefore, that these narratives comprise a mythology of their own; an almost primordial tale of transformation and redemption complete with a hero and villains and phases as predictable as those of the moon.

If these stories could be reduced to their basic elements, if they did constitute a central Myth of the New York Drag Queen, it might go something like this. 1) Young man wakes up one day in the suburban or rural setting in which he has always lived, suddenly to find that his home feels as

Flloyd: A character. You've developed a certain character.

Miss Understood: Yeah, and to me it's like not just a character, it's more of an art project. I see myself as a design thing. I put together the colors of the hair and the colors of the outfit. When I have my clothes made, I go look at these fabrics and I hold them next to each other and I get real picky. I don't just say, "Oh, that's nice." I'm really specific about every little thing.

Chicklet: So why do you care what somebody thinks?

Miss Understood: Oh, I'm just discussing it. I'm not, like, obsessing over it.

Chicklet: No, but you sound like you're feeling underappreciated. You have to get over that, 'cause you're always going to feel that way. It's never going to be like everyone's gonna love what you do or everyone's gonna see what you do. It just isn't like that.

foreign as the salt plains of Mars. This is where he is, has probably always been, but it is not where he is supposed to be. "The sadness of sophistication has come to the boy," wrote Sherwood Anderson—not about nascent drag queens, of course, but the moment is the same. The family, friends and schoolmates with whom he has grown up are as the creatures in a dream, fundamentally recognizable but strangely distant. He likes them well enough, but he knows that they are not like him and, more importantly, do not understand him. They may love him very much, but that love alone cannot outweigh the lack of understanding that fills the days that pass between them. 2) Young man gets it that he cannot stay, that other voices are calling his name; and he must travel to find them. Perhaps a friend needs visiting, a school needs attending or a job needs filling. The reason for leaving, the way out, changes with each individual story, but the destination is the same. Any excuse will do, just get to New York City. 3) Having found a reason to get there, or after having been pulled there by forces of which he might not have even been aware, our hero is plunked down on the island of Manhattan, a hyperactive world of freaks and other misfits. Strange as the landscape may be—and what could be stranger really than the trumped up skyline of New York—it feels more familiar than anyplace he has ever been.

After all, New York calls to you. Like Circe on the rocks, if her song gets through, then forget it, you're hers. New York is and always has been a city of imports; virtually every aspect of it has been shaped by the hands of immigrants. Whether the result of the great foreign migrations of the late nineteenth and early twentieth centuries or the not-so-great yuppie invasion of the 1980s and '90s, much of the look and feel of the world's most impossible metropolis is the result of the energy, alacrity and anxiety of people who often gave up much and fought hard to get there. Living in New York is not unlike, say, turning out gay: many people

Julian: Well, before we finish up, is there anything else that any of you would want to say?

Linda Simpson and **Flloyd:** I hate you!

Flloyd: Jinx!

Chicklet: No, I want to say: Miss Understood, I appreciate what you do, I think what you do is special and real.

Flloyd: As long as we appreciate it, it doesn't matter what those people think.

Flloyd: If you had Candis, Girlina, Misstress, Sherry and Joey, you would have gotten a whole different response. I'm not saying it would be better or worse. It would just be completely different.

Linda Simpson: If you had had Queerdonna, Rita Menu and Constance here—[Laughter.]

Flloyd: And Faux. And Cody. [More laughter.]

Linda Simpson: If you had Cody, Miss Robbie—[Yet more laughter.]

there would rather not have to put up with the struggle, but they likewise cannot deny the deepest part of themselves. It's not the sort of town where one settles down for the sake of it. It's a place that demands as much as it rewards, and given its insatiable appetite for human fodder, really only those whose drive is great enough and whose other options are few enough ever come for more than a visit. New York's own central myth—that of the wide-eyed adventurer, arriving on the dock, a bag in one hand, a hat in the other, a telephone number in his pocket and a whole lotta hope—is still getting a regular workout. In case you thought it was no longer being told, rest assured that its script is being acted out regularly by the neophyte drag queens and budding young actors who stream out of New York's bus and train stations virtually every day of every week.

4) Invariably, our young Odysseus follows an instinctual road to Downtown, discovering along the way the displaced wanderers who are likewise feeling their way around the alien, but undeniably magical, landscape. Like our hero, they found their existence intolerable back on Mars, and wished themselves to this other world where life's passion play gets played out with, well, passion. There is perhaps a shock to our hero's system when he discovers these kindred spirits. It may be a shock of horror at the sight of so many similarly hobbled souls, or perhaps it's one of recognition, of seeing one's own strangeness reflected back in the faces and bodies of New York's many adopted children. There may be a feeling of shame when he first notices the variety of deformities and handicaps that have brought them together here. On a good night, the Pyramid, for example, might easily have been mistaken for the recovery room at one of the city's many public hospitals: crowded, dirty and full of grotesques, all licking the hidden wounds of diversity that sent them packing in the first place.

Miss Understood: You mean Ralph?

Linda Simpson: Connie Girl.

Flloyd: Connie Girl, and Diandra. And Barbara Patterson Lloyd. If you had Lilly and Kabuki, and who else is meager and meek?

Linda Simpson: This is the *worst* encounter group that I've ever had!

Flloyd: No one else would have listened to your long-winded stories.

Chicklet: I felt like the youngest one and so I tried to keep the quietest. You know, when they're talking about those Pyramid days, I'm thinking I was in second grade, so—

Flloyd: How old are you?

Chicklet: I'm twenty-two. I'll be twenty-three in December.

Miss Understood: She's lying! She's lying! Lies, lies, lies.

John Waters
Filmmaker, Author

I'm against the Disneyization of drag queens. I think drag queens should scare families and not make them feel happy about themselves. When Divine started, drag queens were very square. They wanted to be Miss America. There were no hip drag queens. Other drag queens hated Divine because he would show up and try to be Miss America, and he would have fake scarves on and he would be carrying an axe. So I think that, God knows, drag queens now are much hipper than they were. That's the major difference. My favorite drag queen is Paige because she looks like she's having a nervous breakdown. But Paige looks good. Paige is unreadable. I don't know what her demons are but she wears them well. I like the pathological ones that stare at themselves in mirrors while they dance over and over on Special K. Those are the ones I like, scarier ones.

5) If the unconventional family that plays together stays together, then here is where the mythical drag queen/protagonist finds the family with whom he will stay and grow and eventually find himself. Here the budding queen assembles the members of his new family—one which includes mothers, fathers, brothers, sisters and everyone in between. Drag performers routinely hook up with more seasoned queens who in a kind of unofficial ritual take them under their wings, both professionally and otherwise. (See "Queen Mothers.")

Finally our hero begins the transformation that will allow him to confront the parts of himself that were previously forbidden or hidden from view. Different versions of this chapter are written by different people, some more straightforwardly than others. For some new New Yorkers, these days can last for years on end, can be very turbulent and lead to further disillusionment before the protagonists are led back home, to a renewed sense of self. To be sure, these are just the sorts of trials that characterize virtually everyone who has ever lived past the age of thirteen, but there is something about the uniformity and passion of these stories as they are told by queens that lends them a unique intensity and

Flloyd: Quick, what year were you born in?

Chicklet: '71

Flloyd: Oh my God.

Miss Understood: Am I special? I love you!

Linda Simpson: Let's all hold hands. You're my drag queen sisters.

Flloyd: Do you have that ten dollars you owe me, Linda?

Linda Simpson: I think I left that crack pipe in your living room.

Flloyd: Paige took it.

Linda Simpson: [To Miss Understood.] Hedda, I just want to tell you how much I appreciate your act.

Miss Understood: I do think you would have gotten a lot different answers if you invited different people. Like these three have been around for a really long time and come from that whole—

drama. Part of the role of drag queens (like all theater people) must be to live out those human experiences that are most profound and potentially redemptive in a performatory and ironic way that lets the rest of us visit them.

If this is true, if every culture does in fact have fundamental myths that are a reflection of the special ways in which its people inhabit and travel through life, then could this be the myth of the New York drag queen? How does this story, so consistently told throughout the drag community, reflect the transformation that is at the heart of the community's experience? And, since these myths are stories of the central transformation of growing up, could it be that, as gay culture is only in its adolescence, drag has become its myth because it signifies a transformation that is suspended in time?

More than a few people have noted that if there is such a myth for gay life, it was made into a movie years ago—starring Judy Garland, no less. *The Wizard of Oz,* even before it was turned into the cinematic icon that it now is, always reflected the crisis of difference and dislocation that typifies the lives of so many gay people. The sense that there is a magical place where a stranger feels at home, where the oppressive weight of a family's limited expectations is thrown off and a new family embraces one for whom one truly is—all of this is played with magical rightness in Victor Flemming's masterful reworking of Frank C. Baum's classic fantasy. And with Gaydom's Joan of Arc playing the lead, it's little wonder that virtually all gay people have found the movie irresistible. The difference for drag queens specifically is that they go through the story's many phases *actually singing the songs* from the movie and wearing great shoes as they go. For drag queens, *The Wizard of Oz* is less a metaphor for personal transformation than a good script and a series of musical numbers written by Harold Arlen and E.Y. (Yip) Harburg.

Linda Simpson: I haven't been around that long! I started drag in 1989!

Miss Understood: That's a long time compared to the people I'm talking about.

Flloyd: [To Hapi] Well, which one of the three is he talking about? Me or you?

Miss Understood: I'm talking about you and you, and Bunny.

Flloyd: And Hapi.

Miss Understood: And Hapi. That's four people from the Pyramid era, right? I'm somebody that looks *back* to the Pyramid.

Flloyd: Well, Linda is *late* Pyramid.

Miss Understood: Right. So what I'm saying is, I think you would have gotten really different answers from Candis or someone like that.

Linda: All right. Whatever.

Miss Understood: She's twenty-five or twenty-six.

In the final analysis, queens have succeeded, as did Dorothy Gale, in lighting the way for their adoptive brethren and sistern, turning the world on with their smiles and making it all seem worthwhile. They have left something behind, but accrued much along the way. They may not be in Kansas anymore, but they have begun the journey home.

Chicklet: I am not either!

Flloyd: In '71, I bought that first Partridge Family album.

[They prepare to leave.]

Chicklet: Which drag queen do you think he really did not want to deal with while doing this book?

Flloyd: Faux! [Laughter.]

Miss Understood: Flloyd.

Linda Simpson: Well, Faux's a toughie.

[They exit.]

The Profiles

FROM: Minnesota

SPECIES:

AFRODITE

Mighty Afrodite

The Setting: A recent *Wigstock* on the Westside Highway. The Weather: Windy. The Mood: Up. It's Afrodite's big number. In a clingy brown A-line shift with her hair pulled back in a kinky double Afro-puff, she's lip-syncing with all the intensity for which she has justifiably become renowned. After being buffeted all afternoon by strong north-easterly winds off the Hudson, the jerry-rigged ribbon proscenium curtain that crowns the stage collapses, stringing itself across the stage and Afrodite's decolletage. It's one of those classic show biz moments when one of two things can happen: disaster or redemption. Unshaken—nay, inspired—Afrodite displays all of the self-possession and acuity that put her on the top of the heap in the first place. Pulling the broken curtain down toward her midriff, poised like an urban Annie Oakley, she continues to "sing." Grabbing the fallen valance as if it were a gauntlet, she moves her lips, holds her ground and waits until the moment is right. As the music catches up with her, she latches on to its insistent rhythm, rides the wave of the song's growing climax, and then lofts the broken banner over her head and into the wind, which carries it toward the sky—and with it her stock as one of New York's favorite drag stars. The payoff for her courage, patience and economy is immediately apparent: as if she's let go of a magic slingshot the strap of which she's stretched to the very breaking point, her simple move is a dancer's expert release of tension that sends the audience reeling. As her routine spins to a close, the final measures of the song are drowned out by the cheers of her exhausted fans. A day that might have laid waste to another less self-possessed performer belongs to Afrodite • She

M.O.:

RAISED IN: Same	CAME TO NYC IN: 1990	STARTED DOING DRAG AT: 21

comes by her discipline legitimately. As a dancer in St. Paul, Minnesota, the young Andre approached Bill T. Jones, who was touring with his company. Showing considerably more than your average degree of aplomb, he announced to Jones his intention to move to New York, become a professional dancer and join the legendary choreographer's company. All of which he did. • Remarkably soft-spoken for a performer of such power, Afro—as her friends call her—recalls that "the first taste of New York drag I got was *Wigstock* 1990. I didn't know they were men! I had seen some drag in Minnesota, but it was men with burly chest hair, bad lipstick—you couldn't even call it drag, really." While still a newcomer to the East Village scene, friends introduced Andre to the Pyramid, where he befriended the ever increasing **Ebony Jett**. Playing a sort of Thelma Ritter to Ebony's Bette Davis, Afro would accompany Jett to the club where she was starring in a number of different shows and weekly parties. Hanging out at the Pyramid for long enough often leads to drag dreams of one's own and Afrodite was soon caught up in the spell that glamour casts. Having attended to Ebony's costumes, makeup and other queenly accouterments for weeks on end, she had an invaluable headstart in putting together a look of her own. Apparently she managed to skip the usually inevitable "ugly phase" of ill-applied eye shadows, scary wigs and lousy ensembles. **Linda Simpson**'s legendary New Queens on the Block provided the forum in which Afrodite first stunned a crowd some might describe as less than easy to impress. "When you first do it, the homage that you get from people, even if you've always been popular . . . Once you get that instant gratification, that homage—and that money—it really throws you for a loop." The same

Why do you do drag?
When I first started it was the thrill and the excitement of something different. Now I do it for the money.

If someone wanted to start doing drag, what would be the first thing you would tell them to do?
Make sure you're really ready.

Do you try to be "real" in any way when you do drag?
As in real woman? I can't because I don't possess a feminine body, so no. But I work what I have, which I think is pretty special.

EARLY DRAG NAMES: None

FIRST SONG. SUNG OR LIP-SYNCED: *"Monie in the Middle"* (Monie Love)

SISTERS OF THE CLOTH: Misstress

MOTHERS: Raven-O, Blacktress

IF NOT DRAG THEN: Dancing

TUCKS:
☐ YES ☐ NO ☑ SOMETIMES

Plumage

GLAMOUR   CLOWN

simple discipline and dedication that she brought to the dance she now brings to her work as one of New York's most exciting drag performers. Young, beautiful and hardworking, Afrodite, like her erstwhile roommate **The Misstress Formika,** is one of a handful of nascent superstars who have raised the standards of her craft across the board. Her colleagues know that once an audience has experienced her sleek, sexy, polished brand of glamour and style, they are not likely to settle for less. One sees in Afro touches of Diana Ross, Eartha Kitt, and Ann-Margret. She clearly understands the power of the human form and the exaltation that accompanies its glorification. In a scene where lip-syncing is increasingly viewed as retrograde, she reminds even the most vociferous detractor that done properly the form is as valid as ever. • Remarkably, for someone as naturally gifted as she, Afro has begun to limit her appearances. She seems acutely aware that in the end, it's the *character* who's garnered all the praise and fans. It's hard to take the adoration to heart when you're stuffed into a corset and overpriced, size 10 Ferragamos. "I was doing drag all the time, then after a while I was like 'Wait a second, I feel more attractive in drag than I do as a boy. Something's not quite right.' I couldn't let it consume my life. I really just want to concentrate on being a boy, so I think I'm going to take a little break for a while." But then she smiles as she ponders the magic at her command when she really turns it on, and it is apparent that she won't be gone for long. "After all," she says wistfully, more to herself than anyone else, "only drag can give you fantasy."

FROM: North Carolina　　　**SPECIES:**

JOEY ARIAS
Legend

Joey Arias is drag's great anomaly for a number of reasons, chief among them that he uses his real name, that he often focuses on a personae other than his own and that he did not emerge from under the wing of another older queen or group of queens. Rather, he brings to his work a measure of true New York celebrity that most other queens just don't have. Perhaps this is because so many of his age and ilk have died or vanished and he is a rare holdover from a time that by all rights should have swallowed him up. Not only has Joey Arias survived, however, he has prevailed. • In many ways, the drag that Joey is doing now is considerably toned down from the antics that first brought him notoriety. From his earliest days as a youngster in Catholic school, he displayed proclivities that were unorthodox to say the least. He was fascinated by the constricting habits and heavily ritualized behavior of the nuns. While most boys his age were anxious to distance themselves from the sisters' moralizing and penchant for corporal punishment, Joey gravitated toward the ceremonial aspects of the religious life, almost fetishizing its dark garments and the relationship between physical discomfort and spiritual joy. He was eight. By the seventh grade he was hard at work scaring his schoolmates to death by tweezing his eyebrows, bleaching his hair and wearing a dress to graduation. • The son of a homemaker and a paratrooper, Joey soon discovered the many splendors of dropping acid with funk bands and hanging out in L.A. recording studios. By 1976 he had made it safely to New York, where Fiorucci's, the ultra-fashionable clothing store on Fifty-ninth Street, provided him with just the platform (not to mention the platforms) he needed to fully express his creative impulses. With the denizens of such beehives of glamour as Studio 54 and the Mud Club stopping in daily to shop for an evening's rituals, Joey became a sort of indispensable professional shopper to the members of a scene whose decadence was the perfect context for his well-developed sense of glorified decay and gender play. Where before his antics might have spelled expulsion, here they brought him adoration, notoriety and the chance to hang and perform with the artists and rockers who made the scene. For years there was hardly an avant-garde setting in which Joey could not be found. Among others, a long association with David

M.O.: 　　　**BEEN DOING DRAG FOR:** 8 years

| **RAISED IN:** North Carolina | **CAME TO NYC IN:** 1976 | **STARTED DOING DRAG AT:** N/A |

Bowie, Iggy Pop and, especially, musician/performance artist Klaus Nomi yielded tours and recordings and a chance for Joey to leave his indelible impression on industry insiders and star-crazed spectators the world over. • Providence truly took over in 1987, however, while Joey was in Europe on tour with Iggy Pop. Always a fan of Billie Holiday's, and fond of imitating her unique vocal stylings, he was heard backstage one evening warming-up à la Lady Day. As anyone who has ever heard him will attest, the similitude is uncanny, and audiences would soon command him to present entire performances of songs "in the style of" his longtime idol. Management was procured through his friend Elvira (Mistress of the Dark), whom he had befriended (along with Pee-wee Herman) during a stint with the L.A.-based improv comedy group The Groundlings. The Billie Holiday routine grew steadily, although for a long while the performance remained largely disembodied since Joey remained out of drag. A Halloween jaunt in cat eyes, torpedo tits and blond wig soon changed all that—people may have been intrigued by the voice, but they were willing to pay cash for drag. Justine De Sade was born and she could be seen all over town in any manner of compromising, often explicit positions. • Today, Joey has toned down the pornographic aspects of his work, although he is still known to stop mid-song and fellate a microphone or beer bottle. More often, however, he captivates with his regal presence and truly astonishing ability to "channel" Billie Holiday. His many laps around the block have imbued him with a worldly power that leaves fans and performers enthralled. He is, finally, as he puts it, going "where the cosmos leads—at one with the universe."

Why do you do drag?
    Why does the world spin, why do seasons change? Why do drags drag?
    It's natural.

Do you have any sayings or catch phrases that are yours or that you
    consider trademarks?
    I got fucked so hard my cherry turned into a blueberry.

EARLY DRAG NAMES:
    Justine De Sade

FIRST SONG. SUNG OR LIP-
    SYNCED: Tantum Ergo

SISTERS OF THE CLOTH: Raven-0

MOTHERS: Claus Nomi

IF NOT DRAG THEN: Whatever the cosmos wants me to do

TUCKS:
☑ YES   ☐ NO ☐ SOMETIMES

Plumage

GLAMOUR   CLOWN

FROM: Wilmington, NC	**HABITAT:**	

THE "LADY" BUNNY

Georgia Peach

𝓑unny is the most powerful drag queen in New York. As the sole proprietress of the enormously successful *Wigstock,* she is, for better or for worse, the lens through which most of the city, and therefore the world, sees drag. True, **RuPaul** is more famous and **Lypsinka** more accomplished in her own way, but ultimately even the most successful queens are pretty much free agents, scratching and surviving as best they can. But as the mass-media mega-mergers of late have taught us, he who holds the keys to distribution is the one to watch. And Bunny's got 'em. With *Wigstock* bringing more drag to more people in more places than any other single event or medium, she is to drag what ABC is to Disney or Blockbuster is to Showtime: a direct, established conduit to the viewing audience at large. And judging by the look of it, she is no less autocratic than the infamous moguls who rule those other franchises. This authoritarianism is not lost on her colleagues who, once a year, play by her rules or not at all. • Bunny learned early, as they say. Youth was a training ground for the boy who would one day parlay his strangeness into a valuable commodity. Whereas many youngsters wilt under the pressure of there own difference, Bunny discovered that by embracing the things that set her apart she gained power and commanded respect. Of this period, she observes, "Even though I was a total sissy, I was an established sissy." Raised in Chattanooga, he was the product of a whole family of nonconformists,

Photo by Tom Pitts

M.O.:	

RAISED IN: Ghana, London, Atlanta, Chattanooga, TN

which may explain his tight, if unusual, bond with them. Bunny describes his father, a history professor, as "the town liberal" and his mother, a nurse, as "the most lovely and fun Southern Lady." When Bunny was eleven, the family spent a year in Ghana, where his father taught at university and both of his parents became Quakers and vegetarians. When they returned, their neighbors welcomed them home with such time-honored expressions of Southern hospitality as taunts of "nigger lovers" and painted swastikas on the door. But throughout his childhood (and adolescence, much of which was played out in a British boarding school) Bunny's remarkable self-possession and capacity to disarm lent him a measure of immunity to the violence and alienation that so often accompanies youthful nonconformity. • That precocious resilience and unwillingness to wallow in life's uglier vicissitudes went with Bunny to Atlanta—where she fell in with **Flloyd**, **RuPaul** and **Lahoma Van Zandt**— and is reflected in her current outlook. "I'm not saying that there aren't things to change or there aren't plenty of demands that need to be met yesterday, but . . . in the face of AIDS, in the face of discrimination, we're *alive*," she asserts. "Things ain't so bad. There's still a place to buy a joint on the corner and you can still get a wig for under twenty dollars!" • Ah, wigs . . . and the institution that was built on "nothing more than a dream and a few cans of hairspray." Bunny will be the first to admit that as a lunatic migrant from Atlanta—who arrived under the unwieldy moniker The "Lady" Bunny Hickory Dickory Dock Cougar Mellencamp—she never dreamed that she'd become one of the important queens of her day. Like her Georgian compatriots, she landed at the Pyramid something of a mess, devoted to little more than stupidity and a commitment to avoiding boredom. "I went for an idiotic, purposefully artsy effect

On film:
> "After *Kramer vs. Kramer*, that's when I stopped going to see new films. Here's an entire film about divorce and custody, with a plain woman who doesn't have one interesting outfit."

Career Highlights:
Founder: *Wigstock*
Star: *Wigstock the Movie*
Appeared in *Bazaar* with Kate Moss
Appeared at Radio City with the B-52's

EARLY DRAG NAMES: The "Lady" Bunny Hickory Dickory Dock Cougar Mellencamp

FIRST SONG. SUNG OR LIP-SYNCED: "One Monkey Don't Make No Show" (Honeycone)

SISTERS OF THE CLOTH: Lahoma, Flloyd, RuPaul

MOTHERS: Sister Dimention

IF NOT DRAG THEN: Candle Maker

TUCKS:
☑ YES ☐ NO ☐ SOMETIMES

Plumage

GLAMOUR   CLOWN

CAME TO NYC IN: 1983	STARTED DOING DRAG AT: 19

to kind of satirize the artsy New Wave scene. I would arrive at a club with a huge branch in my arms just as a fool! Just to take the piss out who knows what! It was so pathetic!" Pathetic, perhaps, but years ahead of its time. Indeed, *Wigstock* (which—to the chagrin of a number of other performers— is purely an expression of Bunny's fluffy world view) has become an event of such magnitude that, no matter what else she does, her legacy as its founder and impresario will probably forever overshadow her reputation as one of the great virtuosos of her craft. One is not likely to hear another name cited more often by other queens as a favorite performer. When she's really on, Bunny's down-home style, eye-popping ensembles and acetylene wit comprise as outrageous and compelling a piece of performance as anyone is likely to see. Thus the tension that exists for many queens who admire her talent and yet object sotto voce to the iron fist with which she rules over *Wigstock*. To them she responds, "I'm not gonna slave all summer long so that someone can get up there and do something that I don't like . . . I don't want to pander to people's lowest tastes. I want to give them something that is *my* vision." Those who don't agree are forced to lump it, as many can bear witness. Still Bunny is unshakable in her commitment to keeping her baby light, loony and strictly apolitical. She'll admit that it's no easy task, and tougher than it sometimes feels worth. And yet she is cheerfully driven to continue, musing "what an idiotic, stupid, shambles of a pursuit it is for me to involve myself in and spend eleven years of my life doing—but isn't it fun?" Yes, Bunny, it is fun.

| **FROM:** New York | **SPECIES:** | |

CHARLES BUSCH
Queen of the Theater

*I*t's probably unfair to group Charles Busch with the majority of the drag queens found in this guide. He trades rarely, if ever, in the gritty currency of downtown hipness that is the stock and trade of most queens. But in the same way that different species within the same genus or family, whose morphologies differ dramatically, nevertheless share a common ancestral link, Charles Busch and his cousins in the clubs, bars and on cable share many traits. For better or worse, these ancient ties bind them in several ways. But as the only drag performer in New York who could live off of royalties from Samuel French, Inc. (the publisher of his plays) he is, very simply, different. As Busch himself puts it, "I relate more to Fanny Brice than to Jackie Curtis . . . I completely lack any edge," and that alone separates him from the hipper downtown drag scene. Furthermore, as the author of, among other things, the longest running "straight" play in off-Broadway history, *Vampire Lesbians of Sodom,* Busch is the clear successor to the theatrical throne formerly occupied by the otherwise incomparable **Charles Ludlam**. What's more, his relationship to Ludlam is not only a matter of two thespians cut of the same ideological cloth: there is a pedagogical reationship between them that borders on the parental. The two first met while Busch was a callow theater student at Northwestern University. He was, not atypically, a tad too preoccupied with his own

M.O.:

RAISED IN: Same	CAME TO NYC IN: N/A	STARTED DOING DRAG AT: 14

coming of age to concentrate on his studies, and he went in search of adventure. Ignoring whatever academic imperative Northwestern University might have been imposing at the time, Busch and a close friend attended a workshop being given by Ludlam's Ridiculous Theatrical Company during their tour to the Midwest and ended up spending the night with them in their hotel. While they would not meet again until years later when Busch was performing in New York, something like a torch was lit that night. Could either of them have known how vigorously it would eventually be passed? Like Ludlam, Busch's work is theater first, drag second. And depending on who is talking—queens or theater people—the reaction to that notion can be quite strong. Both camps, as it were, are anxious to claim these men as their own. • Busch is an exceedingly articulate and soft-spoken gentleman. Nothing about his offstage demeanor betrays his gift for whipping up the upbeat, gender-bending, B-movie hilarity which he has fairly patented. As a youngster living in Westchester, a solidly middle-class suburb of New York, young Charles was set adrift by the death of his mother coupled with the general unresponsiveness of his father. Lost in a fantasy world of old movies, unable to focus on anything in particular, unsupervised and flunking out of school, he was saved from what he maintains would have been a wayward path by his mother's sister, his Aunt Lillian. Widowed and living in the city, she took him in and set him straight. "She tried to drum into my head that there was a wider world than my own neuroses. That was hard to do . . . so she encouraged whatever talents I might have had. Basically, I owe my whole life to her." • While no two of the roles he writes for himself are ever the same, there is an instantly recognizable "Charles Busch Character" in all of them. She's a 1940s kind of gal, fresh out of a George Cukor wet dream. She is well dressed, beautiful in a manicured way, highly civilized, cultured and camera-ready; a combination Rosalind Russell and Norma Shearer. The lightly clenched jaw seems to be holding back a smile, as if it would be rude to give it full girth. As the author and star not only of *Vampire Lesbians . . . ,*

> *On the theater:*
> "I spent some time doing roles out of drag, but it didn't go so well. I called it my 'lesbian phase.' "

EARLY DRAG NAMES: N/A	MOTHERS: Charles Ludlam
FIRST SONG, SUNG OR LIP-SYNCED: N/A	IF NOT DRAG THEN: Writer
SISTERS OF THE CLOTH: Everett Quinton, Lypsinka	TUCKS: ☑ YES ☐ NO ☐ SOMETIMES

Plumage

GLAMOUR — CLOWN

but also of *Psycho Beach Party, Red Scare on Sunset, The Lady in Question, You Should Be So Lucky* (in which he appeared, less successfully, out of drag), *Swingtime Canteen* and an uproarious novel based loosely on the trials of producing *Vampire Lesbians* . . . entitled *Whores of Lost Atlantis,* he is a true star whose light shines far beyond the relatively narrow borders of New York, drag, or both combined. As far as the much ballyhooed mainstreaming of drag is concerned, it could be argued that counting all of the regional, summer stock and student productions of his wildly popular cross-dressed farces and musicals, Busch has gotten more regular folk to throw on more wigs than any amount of dime-store proselytizing **RuPaul** could ever do.

FROM: Maui	**SPECIES:**

CANDIS CAYNE
The Cyd Charisse of Drag

"*I*'m not the kind of person who could hide my femininity" understates the owner of what are maybe the best set of gams this side of the Pacific. One of the few queens who gives real showgirls a run for their money, Candis clearly enjoys the confusion she creates, but is anxious to assert that it's not for its own sake—there's power in them thar heels! "When I put on my makeup, I can do anything, I can wear anything, I can say anything . . . When I walk into a room as Candis, people stop what they're doing and *look*." Slender, angular and graceful, she is the kind of beauty who regularly stops traffic and turns heads. A reasonably pretty boy out of drag, she is a stunner when she applies a full complement of accouterments and turns the volume all the way up. Paramount among her qualities, as anyone who has laid eyes upon her will tell you, is her exquisite beauty and uncanny female morphology. • Candis, **The Misstress Formika, Sherry Vine** and **Girlina,** sister queens who perform together and who emerged on the scene at the same time, have raised the professional standards of their trade in proportion well beyond their numbers. Due to the high profile of their work and the commensurate demands they regularly make on their clientele, these girls stand poised to turn a once hidden hobby into a high-paying, long-term career. Candis is a leader among a new generation of New York drag queens that is literally changing the face of the profession. In her work there is nary a trace of the shame so evident in the drag of her stigmatized predecessors. She's feminine, athletic, talented and extremely beautiful. Her goals are set and her ethic is professional. She works hard, looks great and gets paid accordingly • Born in small-town Hawaii, she had an upbringing that could not have reflected less the dizzying pace and high-octane glamour of her current life as one of New York's top drag entertainers. What the story of her youth does contain, however, is the trademark

M.O.:

RAISED IN: Same	**CAME TO NYC IN:** 1991	**STARTED DOING DRAG AT:** 19

characteristics of those who lead such a life. She is indeed a friend of Dorothy: one can almost see the young Brendan clutching himself gently, gazing out over the steep cliffs of Maui, dreaming of a world in which his special qualities were an asset and not a dangerous liability—where his angular shape and super-high kicks could be the ticket to widespread adulation rather than exile and ennui. His first chance at fulfilling that dream came in a Maui community theater production of *La Cage aux Folles,* a stroke of good fortune for which the producers must have been as grateful as was he. While stretching out as a Cagelle, Brendan befriended a queen from Los Angeles named **Lana Cayne,** who would eventually bestow upon him two matchless gifts: a name and a way off of Maui. In L.A., Candis would meet and move in with **Sherry Vine** and begin a period she now calls "the funest of my entire life. I had my own room, my own space, my own motor scooter and all the friends a girl could want." A stint on a cruise ship eventually landed her in New York, where she struggled in and out of drag as a waiter and cigarette girl. When she showed up at the Boy Bar one night to sing backup for her friend **Afrodite,** Matthew Kasten describes her as being "a mess," a situation he would soon rectify, eventually grooming Candis into the winner of the prestigious Miss Boy Bar pageant in 1994. • Perhaps it was the motor scooter, but comparisons to Ann-Margret seem inevitable as Candis shakes, shimmies and vibrates her way through her routines. It is probably worth noting that she is one of the few queens working in the city today about whom fellow dragsters have only good things to say. They all admire her style and energy and are clearly inspired by the level and appeal of her work. But that's not surprising given the pleasure she gets out of it. "When you put on your makeup, you let down your inhibitions. You're more bold, you have more power," she says, revealing the thrill at the heart of drag. "And Candis has a lot of power."

How would you describe your style of drag to someone who has never seen you?
Hyper real. In some ways, I like to see how far I can take it.

Career Highlights:
To Wong Foo, Thanks for Everything, Julie Newmar, Assistant Choreographer
Stonewall, Choreographer

EARLY DRAG NAMES: Candy Cayne

IF NOT DRAG THEN: Dancing

FIRST SONG. SUNG OR LIP-SYNCED: "I Want Candy"

TUCKS: ☑ YES ☐ NO ☐ SOMETIMES

SISTERS OF THE CLOTH: Girlina, Bire Briquet

MOTHERS: Raven-O, Matthew Kasten

Plumage

GLAMOUR — CLOWN

FROM: Babylon, Long Island	**HABITAT:**

CHICKLET

Clamour Queen

"You better work it out, cunt!" insists drag's seedy spitfire. For a queen as relatively unseasoned as she is, Chicklet has accrued a large and devoted following. Perhaps this is because she possesses a certain Marilyn Monroe–ish quality. As with Monroe, behind the makeup and tomfoolery (or perhaps in spite of it), there is an an intelligence, even a trace of humanity, in Chicklet's glance that surprises and disarms. The comparison might seem odd at first: her mouth is dirty and her manner crass, and she bears little or no resemblance to that most sainted of feminine icons. But in the same way that Monroe's evanescent charisma and vaguely haunted quality placed her in stark relief to the countless other bombshell starlets of her day, Chicklet's aura hangs in the air longer than expected. Then again, perhaps it's because Chicklet's got a secret. Yes, behind all the hot-blooded, fast-talking, slutty Latina grandstanding, before she spent her nights prancing and vogueing along the derelict piers of Manhattan's West Village, Chicklet was—and this is true—a nice Jewish boy from New York. • "I'm a Jew-a-Rican!" she confesses, only half-jokingly. That there is no actual Latino blood flowing through her veins will come as a surprise to anyone who has seen her onstage or on her weekly broadcast *A Bitch Called Chicklet* on local public access cable television. (The show was canceled after Chicklet slipped some truly shocking pornographic footage past the censors.) By way of explanation she argues, "Let's face it, black and

M.O.:

Latino girls got it goin' on." What this means, of course, is that there are two levels of drag at work here. She's not only sublimating his masculinity, but also his ethnicity—it's a bonus rarely offered by other queens. Then again, most other queens don't seem anxious to keep so much of who and what they are so well hidden, a quality that makes one think she must have plenty worth hiding. • "I don't think I've ever been a nice Jewish boy . . . I think my whole family is kind of cunty, actually," she remarks enigmatically. By this one supposes she means that while most queens are running from something, she might not be running quite as far as it appears. Chicklet's whole life, though, is something of a performance—while it's clear that he's not a woman, he has just about everyone convinced that he is Latina. And while the notion of Jews trying to assimilate is hardly extraordinary, when they appear to want to trade in that status for another even more marginalized one, one wants to know just what's going on. "I've always identified with those who are truly ethnic," adds Chicklet, reflecting a sentiment typical among queens. In other words, just as some men find it liberating to wear a dress, others find it empowering to adopt the attitudes of women who, in the face of myriad cultural challenges, remain strong, forceful and funny. "People like it when you're saucy with them, as long as you're entertaining. Besides," she goes on, "I'm from your typical white-trash neighborhood, really—very mixed. But a totally nonreligious upbringing—I mean completely no religion whatsoever. So I have no ethnicity in actuality and I can just adopt whatever I want to. Like there are times, honey, I am too, too black, and you know, honey, I can be very Puerto Rican when I feel it, and you know, when I'm really in a bad mood, I am so Jewish, honey. I will complain, I will complain. So I guess it's just another way of saying, 'Honey, I'll be what I wish to be.'" That still doesn't explain where she learned to speak Spanish. "I didn't," she giggles. "I just bullshit it really well." • Whatever the inspiration, Chicklet is clearly on to something. Her appeal is largely comic, as she has few other traditional performance skills to recommend her. She is vociferously anti–lip-sync, which is perverse for someone who cannot sing. She'll grant that some queens do it well, but she nevertheless sees it as a recipe for obsolescence. She prefers sketch comedy and song parodies, both of which require cleverness and timing more than musicianship or vocal dexterity. Writing and producing her own material also guarantees that she'll be able consistently to work out the trashier impulses that burn so intensely within her heart. • So in the final

RAISED IN: Same	**CAME TO NYC IN:** N/A	**STARTED DOING DRAG AT:** 19

analysis, who is this strange conglomeration? Who is this Chicklet? "She's a mess, but she's a proud mess. I don't think Chicklet is too concerned with looking real. Chicklet does not care who she offends, as long as she entertains. She's a crowd pleaser. I think she's the nastier, raunchier, more outrageous aspects of me. I just bring them to the forefront and amplify them. I mean, I've been a bitch my whole life, but now I'm getting paid for it!" Looks like somebody's worked it out.

On why he likes trashiness:
"Because it's more fun. Because being respectable is boring. Because everyone's a fuckin' thief and won't admit it, and I'm admitting it. Everyone's a fucking adulteress, everyone's a thief, everyone's a liar . . . in some part of themselves they are. Honey, to repress that and judge other people, if that's your trip, go on. I do not do that."

On seediness:
"When I say, 'seedy,' I don't mean sitting in a trailer eating Hormel ham out of a can. That's not what I mean. It's part of being shady. Having the nastiest thing to say, and getting away with something."

On her look:
"I'm dead-center between clown drag and glamour drag. I call it Clamour."

On making money:
"Tipping is encouraged 'cause a fish gotta swim, but a bitch gotta eat!"

On the best thing about doing drag:
"You can always get a free cab ride."

Career Highlights:
New Year's at Pyramid 1994 and 1995, *A Bitch Called Chicklet*, *Dogs* and other films by filmmaker Jaba-Laba, getting thrown off the air

EARLY DRAG NAMES: Eurika!, Tawdry Meadows, Misty120, Peatri Dish

FIRST SONG. SUNG OR LIP-SYNCED: "Mama Mia" (ABBA)

SISTERS OF THE CLOTH: Hedda, Miss Understood

MOTHERS: Divine

IF NOT DRAG THEN: Drugs

TUCKS:
☐ YES ☐ NO ☑ SOMETIMES

| **FROM:** Brooklyn | **SPECIES:** |

HRH PRINCESS DIANDRA
Hollywood Royalty

*W*hen the iron-fisted impresario of the Boy Bar Beauties, Matthew Kasten, is asked if there was ever a candidate for stardom within his ranks who didn't require comprehensive redesign and retrofitting before she could pass muster, he doesn't hesitate. "Diandra had it down the day I met her. She showed up with a pair of El Senida platforms, the whole nine yards. Really together." (And this from the man who insists that it took the entire fashion industry five years to catch up with the Drag Queens of New York and start pushing matte lipstick.) Meet Diandra and it is instantly clear. She is perhaps the single most beautiful performer in the New York drag world (apologies to the absent). • One of the few New York drag queens who is a native of New York, Diandra is also the only drag queen who expresses any meaningful awareness of what her color might mean to her life. While she insists that she doesn't think in terms of race, she asserts that she will "impersonate anybody who's colored. I hate the term 'African-American.'" Furthermore, she notes that her tastes, even as a youngster, ran toward the white establishment culture, an interest that the folks at home didn't exactly appreciate. "I used to read the *Times* on Sunday . . . I took *The Preppy Handbook* seriously! My family all hated me and called me white." In order to get a fix of the stuff she loved, then, she turned to her seventh-grade teacher, Mrs. Barracano ("a Jewish woman who married an Italian"), who took her to Manhattan, taught her the joys of Bloomingdales and, most importantly, bought her a

M.O.:

RAISED IN: Same	CAME TO NYC IN: N/A	STARTED DOING DRAG AT: 3

subscription to *W* magazine. "Can you imagine? And I read it weekly, learned about all the people, all the places. It was what I wanted to be. So, I became this fierce 'Oreo,' started speaking really proper . . . All I knew was I was going to be out of the ghetto." • The move to "Fashion High School" in Manhattan put into motion not only the dream of freedom from home and family, but also the process of releasing the "closet drag queen" inside. "I became a faggot in my junior year" he says of his high school, where he was a fashion illustration major. But drag was still a long way off. For the time being, life was about clubbing: looking great, featuring killer outfits and going "straight from the cab into the club." That is until late one night (or early one morning depending on your perspective), at the legendary Paradise Garage, a primarily black and Latin dance club that was prototypical of the massive dance barns that would spring up like weeds throughout the eighties. "I was an overdressed club kid. Patti LaBelle hair, Gaultier ensembles; drag queen in training. Paradise Garage was where I came together," she muses nostalgically. Into this maelstrom walked a queen whom for months Diandra had noticed but never approached. **Connie Girl**. When I first met her, I said, 'Who does she think she looks like? That's a man in a dress. Tired shoes, hideous dress. What is that? Shoot it.' So she walks in, all in pink from the shoes to the hair. Now, you know black faggots are the shadiest faggots. They were all reading her! So shady. I mean just reading her. And I was looking at her, saying to myself, 'You know, it takes a lot of nerve to leave your house looking like that.' So I went up to her and I said, 'There's

On life:
    "I am my fantasy of the perfect woman. I am trying to live it as best I can."

On drag:
    "Men and women have different backs."

On first drag experience:
    "I saw Diana Ross on the Ed Sullivan show and the world stopped. And I watched this woman performing, all this lunacy she used to do, and when it was over I kept pointing to the TV like bring her back. She was God to me. When everyone left the house, I threw on a bodice and pretended to be Diana Ross. I grew up with two sisters and was allowed to play dress-up. I made my sisters play the Supremes, but I always had to be Diana."

EARLY DRAG NAMES: None

FIRST SONG. SUNG OR LIP-SYNCED: "Ain't No Party"

SISTERS OF THE CLOTH:
Connie Girl, Guy, Glamamore

MOTHERS: Dorian Corey

IF NOT DRAG THEN: Death

TUCKS:
☑ YES   ☐ NO   ☐ SOMETIMES

Plumage

GLAMOUR   CLOWN

something very courageous about you. I think I like you.' And she was gagging! Around seven in the morning, they were playing 'Love Hangover' and I was doing it. Every breath, every lick. Connie looked at me and said, 'You're a drag queen, Miss Thing.' I said never!" • "A week later, Halloween, I was the backup for Connie at the Boy Bar. We were doing something about gospel women and I got the Holy Ghost, rolled all over the stage. Matthew Kasten came up to me and said, 'Come back tomorrow to do your own show . . . and think of a name.' So I was reading *Bazaar* and they had a list of the ten most beautiful women and Diandra Douglas was one of them. I thought, Diandra, Diandra . . . such a beautiful name. Cute! I'm Diandra! Me and **Perfidia** did our first shows at the Boy Bar on the same night." The rest is history, as they say; Diandra went on to become one of that club's major successes. Her celebrity carried her around the world, performing in clubs from Rio to Tokyo. Currently, she spends the better part of the year in Tel Aviv, of all places, where she is something of a Semite's Josephine Baker. "They all think I'm a real woman. I'm amused by this because I'm just a tall man who wears lots of makeup." And Big Ben is just a clock. As for her life being just about the farthest thing from what she could have imagined while paging through the *Times* and *The Preppy Handbook,* she remarks without a hint of regret, "I think I was just meant to do what I am doing. It was ordained from the gods. I am a queen. I have small feet!"

FROM: Dominican Republic | **SPECIES:**

DOLORES
Renaissance Queen

$\mathcal{D}$olores will be the first to tell you she's a spicy dose of Latina salsa on a steamy summer's night. But don't come looking for homogenized retreads of Gloria Estefan or Selena if you search for her. Celia Cruz meets Diana Vreeland on crack is more likely to be what you find. And what a refreshing presence she is. Her creator, booster, agent and, some might venture, better half, Hamlet Manzueta, notes, not unwisely, that Dolores caught on specifically because "there wasn't a juicy Latin character downtown." In outlining her development, he echoes the personal stories of many of his peers, describing the halting, often less than graceful way in which this Dominican hot tamale evolved into the international sensation she has now become. What began as an evening of drag on a lark took Hamlet to the Boy Bar, where that club's infamous and charismatic manager dubbed him, typically, "genius." Under Matthew Kasten's heavy hand, Hamlet became Ophelia, a character who is not greatly missed. It appears that this self-starter was in no mood to be circumscribed according to someone else's vision. The Boy Bar experience left a salty taste in Hamlet's mouth and he kept clear of the whole drag scene for over a year. • Meanwhile, Hamlet kept himself busy with the few thousand other professions he's mastered along the way. "I've always liked to do everything," says this graduate of the Fashion Institute of Technology. He has delivered pizza, modeled nude, designed jewelry, made hats, shown his art, produced his own soon-to-be-syndicated cable program, *The Pot,* and holds down a permanent position creating designs for Fila. "I'm an angel," he says without a trace of pretense. This little tidbit he offers during the chic

M.O.:

RAISED IN: Same	CAME TO NYC IN: 1982	STARTED DOING DRAG AT: 29

opening of *Glamour Is Fear,* a sprawling collection of works by downtown artists which he curated as part of the 1995 N.Y. Soho Biennial. Given the number of projects with which he is involved, the intensity and quality of those works and the low-key blitheness with which he carries it all off, one might be tempted to agree that he is at least angelic. • Flash backward to 1990. **Linda Simpson** is cranking up *New Queens on the Block,* a weekly offshoot of her seminal *Channel 69* productions, at Pyramid. Dumping Ophelia for the saucier Lola, Hamlet reemerged in an homage to the femme fatales of the Latin soap operas that dominate the hazier regions of cable television. She was an instant hit, chewing up the sets as well as other queens. As well as Lola went over, however, it wasn't until 1991 that Hamlet, ever the restless artist, realized that yet another voice was calling out to him; that like Ophelia, Lola was merely a phase in a larger evolutionary process. • That voice belonged to a woman from Hamlet's childhood in the Dominican Republic. She was the extravagant daughter of a Dominican ex-president, a neighbor who would leave her home for evening functions in a limousine, self-consciously impressing the hell out of everyone in sight. Her every purchase was a topic for discussion by the entire neighborhood. Just one of her colorful ensembles might include gold Gucci sandals, jewel-encrusted sunglasses and a red, white and blue sarong. That woman's name was Dolores—and she, by all appearances, is alive and well and living on Twenty-third Street. She found her first audience at **Mona Foot**'s *Star Search,* where after winning several weeks in a row, she shifted into the role of Mona's unofficial sidekick. The partnership was a fruitful one and Dolores gained numerous new fans, but it has been her appearances as a truly not ready for primetime player on Hamlet's weekly cable montage, *The Pot,* that has brought her to the attention of fans the world over— literally. • "Dolores is one of the many things I do," says Hamlet, every inch the artist with palette in hand. "She is her own entity. I've incorporated her into my video show as a character, a skit or a segment of the program." Given the warmth with which Hamlet remembers his colorful neighbor, not to mention the entire retinue of powerful female figures from his youth, you might wonder at the clownish nature of his characterizations. To be sure, the fast-talking, street-walking Dolores may be a cartoon version of the woman from his childhood, but Hamlet seems to know that he doesn't really have a choice. "First of all," he argues, "I'm a man, so it doesn't matter how much I try not to go to the extreme. I'm going to look like an extreme. It doesn't matter how 'real' I try to look. I'm going to look like a man." Furthermore, he contends that it is simply more fun this way. "I'm about humor and comedy. I put lipstick on because it's funny and it looks good." The real tip-off, however, only the connoisseur would notice. "I wear my shoes with open toes. I make sure that my toes are sticking out. If I wanted to be real pussy, then I would make sure that my toes were inside my shoes!"

How are you different from other drag queens in New York?
   "I'm Dolores."

On herself:
   "There are all these fun elements that society doesn't allow men to play with because they are for women, and that is what I enjoy about doing drag."

EARLY DRAG NAMES: Ophelia, Lola

FIRST SONG. SUNG OR LIP-SYNCED: "Mambo Bacan" (Sophia Loren)

SISTERS OF THE CLOTH: Linda Simpson

MOTHERS: None

IF NOT DRAG THEN: Drag

TUCKS:
☐ YES ☑ NO ☐ SOMETIMES

Plumage

GLAMOUR   CLOWN

FROM: Atlanta | **SPECIES:**

FLLOYD

King of the East Village Freaks

"*I* think people are intimidated by me," speculates Flloyd. He goes to say, however, that he wants "to be remembered as an artist with integrity and a person of compassion." While no one could argue with the former remark, the latter seems harder to swallow given Flloyd's penchant for scaring the bejeezus out of people. The strange distance between Flloyd's soft-spoken sincerity and his often horrifying performances leaves one with the sense that this fellow who describes himself as having been the "class clown" is struggling with some potent demons. It's as if he has borne witness to something awful and is cursed to keep its ghost at bay by abstracting and reenacting it over and over in perpetuity. He is as well known for being bitter and petulant as he is for his bravura performances as everything from tortured housewives to gothic gargoyles— many of which include such disturbing rituals as self-scarification, vomiting and lighting his own hands on fire. Juxtapose these mortifying exercises with the straightforward assertion that "comedy has always been very important to me; I'd rather make people laugh," and one has some sense of the conflict working within this man. • "I've been doing drag my whole life. I always wore my mom's clothes . . . I wore her wigs . . . The first time I did drag in public I was fourteen," he says, adding "I hate to say it,

M.O.:

RAISED IN: Same	**CAME TO NYC IN:** 1983	**STARTED DOING DRAG AT:** 14

but a lot of the drag I do is based on *The Rocky Horror Picture Show*." An independent spirit from the get-go, he moved out of the house "the day I graduated from high school." He lived on next to nothing in midtown Atlanta, working occasionally at Popeye's, relying on the occasional largesse of his parents, even turning a trick once or twice. One evening in a park, Flloyd and a couple of itinerant friends were approached by a stranger who would come to dominate Flloyd's life as a friend, role model and troublemaker: **RuPaul**. "He was tripping on acid," recalls Flloyd. "He said he'd had a vision of being murdered by four white people and being thrown in a lake. We became really good friends almost right away." Their friendship was on again, off again for some time and was in the off-again phase when Flloyd met, fell in love with and started dating the man who later become known as **The "Lady" Bunny**. "New Year's of 1983 [in Atlanta] I met Bunny at the Nightery. I guess we fell in love . . . I got a crush on him. When I met him, he was wearing this weird Superman outfit: blue sweatpants, and a red sweatshirt and a tacky 'Fourteenth Street' yellow belt. He had these falsies he was using for shoulder pads. He really wanted to meet **RuPaul**." Flloyd reluctantly arranged the meeting, during which he and **RuPaul** were quickly reconciled and the three became, as Flloyd puts it, "inseparable." By his own admission Flloyd can be "very hateful, but very forgiving," and the trio spent several now somewhat infamous years engaging, enraging and otherwise terrorizing the citizens of Atlanta. (Be certain to ask any of them about Casper the Ghost.) • As a member of that notorious Atlanta drag "mafia"—

On his own style:
    "You have to stir up human emotions in order to get people thinking. That's why I've always preferred the weird 'thing.'"

On his enduring friendship with RuPaul
    "We're gonna get high and die!"

Career Highlights
    Nine out of eleven *Wigstocks*
    Eleanor, his one woman show at Pyramid
    Toured with Black Lips Performance Cult
    Hosted the Spew Festival at the Kitchen in Soho

EARLY DRAG NAMES: None

FIRST SONG. SUNG OR LIP-SYNCED: N/A

SISTERS OF THE CLOTH:
    Linda Simpson

MOTHERS: RuPaul

IF NOT DRAG THEN: Film

TUCKS:
    ☐ YES   ☐ NO   ☑ SOMETIMES

which also included **Lahoma Van Zandt** and **Larry T** (not a drag queen, but a member of the drag-o-philic band **Now Explosion**)—Flloyd's first trip north to perform at the Pyramid's "Hotlanta Weekend" was in the Summer of 1983. "When I came to NY and I saw the Pyramid, I realized that I wasn't the only one," he recalls, referring less to drag queens in general than to the "darker, weirder" performance "artists" who interested him but simply did not exist down south. Clearly, however, the Pyramid was never the nurturing haven for Flloyd that it was for so many others. "Bunny got swept under the wing of [club manager] **Sister Dimention,** so she didn't have to worry; the Pyramid was making so much money then. Meanwhile me and Ru were sleeping in Abingdon Square Park . . . or in Central Park or at people's houses." • However, despite their enduring friendship, **RuPaul**'s indomitable charisma proved a difficult obstacle to Flloyd's own creative development. "Ru would always say 'Try to look pretty,' that was his thing. But I never cared about pretty, I never wanted to look real. We had very different agendas. And he has always been the most determined person I've known . . . Being his sidekick was really hard. I remember going with him to Area; I was really trying to look pretty and I was walking around with this plastic smile on my face. I went in the bathroom and I took off my wig and was like What am I doing? I am not having fun, it's not working, it's all bullshit." • This sense of alienation, even from his closest friends, might at least partially explain the aura of bitterness that seems to surround Flloyd, lingering in the air around him like the smell of cigarette smoke in clothes, and informing even his most lighthearted performances. He is a very tough nut to crack, assuming the worst about virtually everything and everyone he encounters. Guilty Until Proven Innocent seems to be his credo. Even the people he cares for are targets of an animus he can't help but manufacture. ("I love **Misstress Formika,** I just don't want her to know it. We're really friendly to each other, but I love to trash her behind her back" is a typically perverse sentiment from Flloyd.) This overwhelming sense of existential ennui is also what makes Flloyd's work great. And there are even signs that he may be mellowing a bit, opening up and feeling more whole. As he looks to a future as a filmmaker, he notes that his Saturn Return is recently whole. He is soft-spoken and bright-eyed as he invokes the astrological precept of which the inescapable **RuPaul** has always been fond. "You're supposed to spend the first twenty-eight years of your life learning, and your next twenty-eight doing. So who knows?"

FROM: Brooklyn | **SPECIES:**

MONA FOOT
Glamazon

$\mathcal{T}$o say that Mona Foot lip-syncs is to say that the Plaza is a hotel, that Midas was wealthy or that Kiss was just a band. She doesn't simply mouth the words, she rides a song like a cowboy rides a bronco. She penetrates it, bends it to her will and, in the end, interprets it with such energy and authority that one feels the song has been given legs at least as much as she's been given a voice. Great vocal performances are simply better when Mona mouths them. Imagine having heard Tchaikovsky's *Nutcracker* but never having seen it danced . . . and then one day the Kirov comes to town. Such is the inimitable power of Mona's fancy footwork. She clearly understands the extremes to which the singers she interprets will go. She has mastered the quivering jaw of a vibrato gone out of control, the hysterical, gaudy, graspiness of a dying disco diva's swan song and the high-kicking, neck-waving, three-snaps-and-you're-out intensity of a strong woman who knows what's hers is hers and what's yours is probably hers too. The fans, of course, adore her for it and flock to her appearances, where she manages the neat trick of making onlookers feel silly and hip at the same time. • "A lot of Mona is my mother," relates Nashom, Mona's strapping other half. "She was so hot when I was young. She had sunglasses for every day of the week, and she wore wigs." To see Mona in full regalia, however, is to know that this is not the whole story. "As a child, I was always into superheros and secret agents and futuristic stuff," she continues, extruding a style of vocabulary that includes not only Twiggy-era mod, but also Barbarella torpedo tits and space-age metallica. Out of drag, Nashom is no less eye-popping, with his enormous and well-

M.O.:

developed physique and always stylish ensembles. For him, though, it's all in a day's work. "To be completely and believably one thing and then turn around and gag everyone and be completely the other thing and do it really well—I love that." Two other, more fateful facets also set Mona apart: she is black and she is from New York, two characteristics she shares with only one other queen, **HRH Princess Diandra**, although that is largely where the similarities end. • She radiates neither the over-weaning ambition nor the determined focus so typical of those other scene-makers who qualify for the category of Impresario, but indeed Mona Foot's work birthing baby queens is second only to **The "Lady" Bunny**'s, **Linda Simpson**'s and that of her own mentor, Matthew Kasten. She never set out to become such (she'll be the first to tell you) but she struck paydirt both for herself and for the community as the hostess of the hugely successful *Mona Foot's Star Search* at the Crow Bar, a diminutive, dimly lit East Village haunt which—along with its sister bar Barracuda—has taken up some of the slack left by the loss of the Pyramid as the bosom of New York drag. "*Star Search* has been one of the best times of my career. And the best thing about that show," says Mona with her mouth full, "is that you only have to pay the winner!" The talent show format is simple and straightforward; contestants are judged according to no specific criteria, only by the volume of audience applause. **Girlina, Sherry Vine, Dolores, Baby Jane Doe**—these are but a few of the callow comers who used the minuscule stage and finicky sound

system of *Star Search* to launch careers that now, one hardly need mention, have all but swallowed up the whole of Manhattan. • Working out regularly, turned on by the notion of living at both ends of the physical spectrum, expertly working a mouth that could easily swallow a fetal pig, Mona comes on a little like Naomi Campbell on testosterone: gorgeous but scary. "I love the idea of looking like a comic book character," she says, recalling that as a kid "that was all I ever looked at." Whether he's Nashom sporting his superhero physique working days selling clothes in a hip downtown boutique, or Mona Foot darting about the galaxy as the Barbarella-influenced "Space Cunt," s/he features a Sabrina-esque joi de vivre that's truly infectious. Nashom is pursuing a record deal with a band of which he is the lead vocalist—a task made easier by his longtime association with funk sensation Dee-Lite. But lest we fear that he might eschew Mona altogether, he asserts reassuringly, "I love drag. I love it, I love it, I love it, I love it! Could I get some more bread, please?"

How would you advise "civilians" about how to start up a conversation with you?
   Tell me how beautiful I am."

On herself:
   "Mona is an independent, strong, black woman. Strong and powerful. She wants things her way—and she gets it!"

On his body:
   "I want to look like a comic book character."

On work:
   "Occasionally she gets a call on the phone and her presence is needed and she goes. She goes where she's needed. Especially when she needs the money."

Career Highlights
   Wigstock at Union Square
   Space Cunt, Space Age Superhero
   Member, Boy Bar Beauties
   Mona Foot's Star Search

EARLY DRAG NAMES: None

FIRST SONG. SUNG OR LIP-SYNCED: "Rock Steady"

SISTERS OF THE CLOTH: Afrodite

MOTHERS: Matthew Kasten

IF NOT DRAG THEN: Washing machine repair

TUCKS:
☑ YES ☐ NO ☐ SOMETIMES

Plumage

GLAMOUR   CLOWN

| **FROM:** Santa Fe | **SPECIES:** | |

THE MISSTRESS FORMIKA

Auto-Erotic Dominatrix

" *I* don't have any tolerance for homophobes and heterophobes," barks The Misstress Formika. "If you're gay and you can't handle straight people, then you need to realize that without them, your faggot ass wouldn't be here!" On the other hand, she goes on, "If you're straight and you can't handle gay people then you have really serious issues to work out."
Marsha P. Johnson would be proud. With her explosive charisma, whip-smart sense of style and intuitive ability not only to ride the latest cultural wave but also to stir up some serious breakers of her own, this downtown dominatrix stands poised to take over the entire world. Of all the candidates grooming themselves for mass consumption, eyeing the prize first fashioned by **RuPaul,** none seems more connected, prepared or naturally right for the role than the Misstress. She may not even be the most talented, strictly speaking, but there's no substitute for pure star power, which she's got in spades. As hostess and emcee at the fiendishly popular *Squeeze Box,* a glammed-out night of rock-and-roll faggotry hidden away in the no-man's-land between the Village and Tribeca, Formika has captured the imagination of hip style makers and trendy consumers alike. Her combination of youthful militance, exquisite beauty and take-no-prisoners variation on a theme of peace, love and harmony has succeeded in forging an entirely new coalition of drag followers, one which comprises of a broad cross-section of scene seekers and makers alike. • If Formika does make it, it will have been well deserved. If there is one queen who embodies the contemporary drag scene's unapologetic ambition it is she. About rescuing the profession from the abyss of shame in which it has been lost for decades she is characteristically clear. "It got to the point where we [Girlina, Sherry and Candis] coordinated our salaries. We said, 'No, we won't do a show for fifty dollars. That doesn't cover my costume, wig and cab. Fuck you. That is so rude to ask me to do a show for fifty dollars.'" Her Norma Rae routine, so well oiled at this point, still doesn't completely explain her popularity. Perhaps it is her open embrace of the glam/punk esthetic that lends her style an unexpected macho punch. She herself doesn't radiate masculinity per se but

M.O.:

RAISED IN: New Mexico	CAME TO NYC IN: 1988	STARTED DOING DRAG AT: 23

her straightforward politicizing and bent toward hard-core rock and roll have opened up a space for gays and their admirers that had been almost forbidden. It's as if she's "outed" a whole segment of the gay population that was somehow compelled to hide its affinity for anything other than show tunes, retro-disco and, perhaps that most virulent of musical plagues, "techno." Even before the smashing success of *Squeeze Box* (and its cousins Fraggle Rock and Rock and Roll Fag Bar), which has landed the Misstress on the pages of practically every major style rag in circulation, her liberating mix of Jerry Garcia–style pot/politics and hard rock music caught on in smaller, more intimate downtown hangouts. She seems to have been aware for some time that urban gay life, for all its flamboyance, can be as confining as any other seemingly less subversive lifestyle. Armed with that knowledge, she has opened and embodied an entirely new marketplace of gay ideas and identity. • She is not to be fucked with, by the by, so don't try. Formika's figured out that power is where you find it. Loud and loquacious, she'll bulldoze over anyone with the gall to cross her or disagree. "I've had gay men come up to me and say, 'I went to *Squeeze Box* last Friday and it was weird.' And I say, 'What do you mean it was weird?' And they say, 'Well, it was just a weird crowd.' And I say, 'Well, it was pretty straight last week.' And they say, 'Yeah!' But you know what? If you're a gay man and you can't come and hang around a straight environment, then I don't want you there . . . The kind of people I want there are gay and straight people who don't have

On how she got into drag:
  "I do drag because when I first came to NYC I saw Lady Bunny and RuPaul at the Love Machine and I thought, Goddamn, I hate waiting tables, I hate going to see those damn auditions, goddammit, I want a fun job . . . The first thing I thought was: What a fun job. I wonder how much money they make."
On her name:
  "Hard, but easy to clean!"
Career Highlights:
  Hostess, Hippie Chix, Global Thirty-Three and Squeeze Box
  Wigstock the Movie
  God Shave the Queen, a compilation on Swoon Records
  Charlie, Theater Couture

EARLY DRAG NAMES: Mica

FIRST SONG. SUNG OR LIP-SYNCED: "I've Got You Under My Skin" (Neneh Cherry)

SISTERS OF THE CLOTH: Candis, Girlina, Sherry

MOTHERS: None

IF NOT DRAG THEN: Watch TV

TUCKS:
☐ YES ☐ NO ☑ SOMETIMES

Plumage

GLAMOUR   CLOWN

issues about their sexuality." There is hardly a position out there that she hasn't got an answer for. Of particular interest is her response to those feminist voices which object to the very idea of drag. "Drag queens aren't anti-feminist. They demonstrate that femininity does not have to equal powerlessness. Why are [they] making claims to high heels and dresses they don't like? Why, now that I have it on, is it theirs? I don't think those are women's clothes; I think they're drag queens' clothes." Don't agree? Don't bother—she's got you outnumbered.
• Perhaps The Misstress Formika can be best understood vis-à-vis the story of her name. Her given name is Michael and, as such, she first became The Misstress For-Michael. The next step was an easy one. "She is the Misstress who dominates her own life, The Misstress Formika." And therein lies a tale. "I want to teach people to dominate their own lives as I have dominated mine." Get to it.

FROM: New York	**SPECIES:**

GIRLINA
Drag Neologist

Girlina is that rare flower who doesn't leap to make assurances that drag is separate from the rest of her life. On the contrary, she prefers the term "gender illusionist," specifically as a means of separating her attitude from that of other drag queens. How, precisely, is a gender illusionist different from a drag queen? "If you look at Lady Bunny and you look at me, you don't see the same thing," she explains. "You see maybe a few traits— we're both performers, we're both icons in singing—but that is as far as the line can be drawn. She is a drag queen and she is happy being a drag queen. She is a fierce drag queen. I, on the other hand, am a *gender illusionist*. I am accentuating my own natural beauty. I am not adding a facade or a clown mask, not that she is, but I am not hiding myself. I can easily be identified outside of my accentuation in the daytime just as well as I can in the evening time." She's right too. For Girlina, all the world's a stage. Chelsea's just got brighter footlights. • This "24–7" ethic might easily push another less polished, less ambitious soul over the edge and into the sort of permanently transgendered territory that most queens are eager to avoid. After all, despite the fact that they rarely work in the conventional theater, drag queens are essentially theatrical creatures and they know it. It follows then that Girlina's all-around, well, *girlishness* might pose a threat to the sacred line that

M.O.:

RAISED IN: Same	CAME TO NYC IN: N/A	STARTED DOING DRAG AT: 23

separates a performer from her audience—a crucial division that most queens struggle to keep intact. Not so. Girlina embraces the chill her all-day flamboyance engenders in so many gay people. And in response to the mockery she occasionally faces, she bites back. "It's a form of repression throughout the gay community. [Gay people] say that we can't come together with this, when in reality they're living for it. And you know they're pressed up in it come Halloween." As she dispenses these simple truths, she smiles the sly smile of someone who has mastered the art of counting cards; she knows the game, the rules and the deck. If you've got it, she can trump it. • Despite her separatist stance, she is a favorite among the other New York queens. With her unique vitality and impenetrable good cheer, she is widely credited with having almost single-handedly revivified the drag scene when she arrived several years ago. Her energy, talent and indefatigable commitment to enlightening as she works have ratcheted up the standards for just about everyone who has shared a stage with her. Perhaps most notable among her achievements is the contribution of an entirely new lexicon which, try as they may, other queens seem unable to avoid. When **Candis Cayne,** for example, tells you that cruise-ship work is "fine for a swirl but not for a spell," or **Chicklet** complains that **Miss Understood** "is so tangie (pronounced TAN-jee)" they are speaking what is known among the ranks as *Girlingo*—really! And there's no getting around it. Girlina herself adds, with an air of performance, "In our faggotry scene, honey, we seem to have so much drama-conflama that we need to come together, trust! So leave the tanginess, sugar, and press up into some tasty ooh-la-la, sugar, trust!" Careful, it's contagious. • A native of the greater New York area, she

Career Highlights
  Swirl, her night at Crow Bar
  "Queen Soul," single cowritten with Paul Alexander
  Girlingo, a language all her own
  Always Something Better, a film also starring Candis Cayne

On Girlina's mission:
  "Before I decide to go anywhere else with my career, I really want to make it comfortable for anyone of any color, any race, any sexual orientation. I want to make them feel comfortable in the gay community."

EARLY DRAG NAMES: None

FIRST SONG. SUNG OR LIP-SYNCED: "Want Some Lovin' You Need Some Loving"

SISTERS OF THE CLOTH: Candis

MOTHERS: Mom

IF NOT DRAG THEN: Nothing

TUCKS:
☑ YES ☐ NO ☐ SOMETIMES

𝒫lumage

GLAMOUR CLOWN

insists that she's been called Girlina ever since her grandmother gave her the name when she was seven. If any of her friends or colleagues knows her original given name, then they're not telling. It's a part of Girlina's gestalt; she sticks by the notion that putting herself out there in an open and consistent way helps/forces the gay community to come to terms with itself and its demons. • Her work in the service of brotherhood, sisterhood and neighborhood not withstanding, however, Girlina's performances can reach a level of profanity, explicitness and hyperactive sexuality that has to be seen to be believed. When she's not lip-syncing to graphic rap songs about what you'll be doing to her "pussy," she often lip-syncs to her own voice, having recorded the dialogue days before a performance and memorizing it in the interim. It is not easy to reconcile the mellow, beat-poet of the newly Castro-converted Eighth Avenue with the writhing, sweating, cursing creature that she can become on stage, yet the connection is there. A gender illusionist like Girlina sees herself as a mouthpiece for a pent-up people as well as the visual projection of all the color and drama of their consciousness. And for all the fire she can breathe while performing, lip-syncing oral phone sex with a phantom caller or preaching about her genitals, during lunch the next day she softly wishes everyone the very best. If it all seems a little hard to believe—the unshakable optimism, the uncanny self-possession, even the balanced romantic life (a true anomaly among New York drag queens)—don't bother trying to dig deeper. She's at least a few steps ahead of that game. As her star begins to rise in earnest, she thinks about her bright future with the same cool enthusiasm with which she considers her past and present. "I'm just like anybody else. I sit on the toilet, I shit and I pay bills. But I enjoy my work. My mom said get a career not a job; I got a career and I love my work. And it makes it fun to go to work if you do." Would we all could be so happy . . . Trust!

BEEN DOING DRAG FOR: 7 years

FROM: Newport Beach, CA	**SPECIES:**

MISS GUY
Acid Queen

She's not the type you want to run into when you're alone in a dark alley, but if you need someone dependable next to you in a foxhole, Miss Guy is your man. Riding the cresting wave of the New Gay Rock movement, she is drag's hard-core pussycat, a bad-ass superstar with a heart of gold. Guy's life has played itself out as a fable, really, about a boy who leaves his home far behind, only to discover that he never left. Her many nights as one of the Boy Bar's reigning beauties, while clearly fulfilling in their own right, were just a tight passage on her way to the rock superstardom that her father had originally chased but which she now seems more likely to achieve. As a boy, Guy was exposed to the wonders of popular music by a father who was a member of one of surf music's greatest ensembles, The Centurions, a long-defunct group whose stock has enjoyed considerable reevaluation recently because filmmaker Quentin Tarantino featured their music on the soundtrack of his film *Pulp Fiction*. As part of another group, The Glass Key, Miss Guy's father opened on the road for Ike and Tina Turner. This is probably when Guy's penchant for seedy, seventies-style variety-show glamour was incubated. Where better to learn the ins and outs of being down and out than on the road with glam rock's most notorious wrecking crew. • If Guy seems strangely disinterested in the notion of gender, it's because for him the issue has always been musical. The glam rockers of the seventies and eighties—David Bowie, Elton John, Kiss, Tina Turner, Boy George and Bow Wow Wow (!)—were his idols mainly because they gave so much when they performed. "I just never had any respect for bands that got onstage in what they wore that day to the sound check." Drag became a journey of sexual identity as well as a way to engage his father's musical legacy. "The main reason I started doing drag was that if I wasn't going to be a rock star, then I would at least dress like my favorites." Of course, dressing like David Bowie when you are not David Bowie is, essentially, to be a drag queen—and Miss Guy quickly became a Big Apple favorite. Often seen in tandem with the scary **Jo Jo Americo,** they combined the best of gender play and high-distortion electric guitar to forge an entirely new kind of rock-and-roll drag—edgy, manic and dangerous. In so doing, they bulldozed over any residual myths of the drag queen as limp-wristed *pathetique.* • When you visit Miss Guy's home, the first

M.O.:

RAISED IN: San Diego	**CAME TO NYC IN**: 1985	**STARTED DOING DRAG AT**: 18

thing you notice is the record collection. It is huge, exotic and thoroughly fabulous. One of a growing number of drag queen DJ's, Miss Guy has eschewed the monotonous and regrettably pervasive machine-like strains of cheap house music or "techno" for the headier and heavier sounds of Hendrix, Bowie and even The Beatles. In the same way that many queens theorize that the recent rise of drag is, at least in part, a reaction to the puritanism of the Reagan/Bush era, Guy sees the success of his reinvention of glam rock as a reaction to the dreary proletarianism of the grunge scene. "I think drag fits into rock because it's very showy. It goes back to the glitter days of Bowie and Alice Cooper and the New York Dolls." In his role as DJ at *Squeeze Box,* the phenomenally successful weekly rock-and-roll drag party in the lower West Village, Guy has taken full advantage of his opportunity to redefine the queer nightlife sensibility by injecting it with a dose of genuine, hard-core testosterone. In the process, he and partner **The Misstress Formika** have created something of an anachronism: a club in which a vigorous mix of genders, orientations and proclivities converge around the ideals of hipness, glamour and performers who always give one hundred percent. The scene is a throwback to a not-so-long-ago era in which one's preference for the same gender mattered less than one's desire for an honest to God good time. "Jayne [County] and Lee [Childers, David Bowie's

On drag:
    "It's the only way to keep the pumped-up gym queens off me!"

On glamour:
    "Lots of makeup, gorgeous hair, beautiful clothes, expensive shoes, feathers, glitter, me!!!!"

On musicians and their clothes:
    "I always loved the idea of having a different outfit for the stage, you know like stage clothes and street gear."

Career Highlights
    Touring with his band, The Toilet Boys
    DJ at Sqeeze Box
    Member of The Bay Bar Beauties
    The Electric Urn, an independent feature film
    Makeup artist and stylist for countless fashion and style magazines

EARLY DRAG NAMES: Guy

FIRST SONG. SUNG OR LIP-SYNCED: "Hooray for Hollywood"

SISTERS OF THE CLOTH: Bunny, Lilly, Sherry

MOTHERS: International Chrysis

IF NOT DRAG THEN: Serial killer

TUCKS:
☐ YES   ☐ NO   ☑ SOMETIMES

Plumage
GLAMOUR   CLOWN

BEEN DOING DRAG FOR: 10 years

mid-seventies tour manager] were telling me how everybody mixed. Rock stars, models, actors, musicians, freaks, drag queens, everybody—at Max's Kansas City, CBGB's and the Mud Club. And then came the eighties and everything became so segregated. Oh and Studio 54 too." If the grunge ethos so popular of late represents a kind of ennui sweeping the youth of the nation, then a return to the highbrow, glamorous androgyny of the seventies might signify a new hopefulness about, if not the future as a whole, then at least about tonight. • Meanwhile, Guy and his band the Toilet Boys seem well on their way to achieving the stardom of which he and his father have always dreamed. Already a veteran of several tours, including *Lollapalooza,* Guy is combining his own personal legacy, a razor-sharp sense of style honed after years of blending rock and drag in the heart of Manhattan's downtown style vortex, and an impressive roster of industry connections to get his dream off to a rip-roaring good start. To wit, he observes, rightly, "When you're onstage, people are paying to see you; you have to give them as much for their money visually as you do musically. I've always been into that." And how.

FROM: Yonkers	SPECIES:

HATTIE HATHAWAY
Historian

*L*ove Hattie Hathaway for using words like "weltschmertz." "It's kind of untranslatable," she says, "but it sort of means 'world-weariness' and that's a word I would use to describe the seventies." It's a good word, too, one that also describes Hattie's own gestalt and perhaps her fascination with that gloomy chapter of New York's history—but weltschmertz? "Well, I'm a little older and I do read," she chuckles, implying that relative to many of her younger cohorts she is considerably more literate and appreciative of history. • Drag queens don't like to age themselves (then again who does) but given the ephemeral nature of their culture and their lives, first-person testimonials are often all one has to rely on when piecing together their story over the long term. Hattie Hathaway is routinely alluded to by other performers as the most reliable source of serious drag history. To discover, then, that she is in fact as young as she is is to see just how fragile the world of drag truly is. • A glance at her CV reveals why she is the undisputed curatorial voice of the New York drag scene. True she's only in her late thirties, but in drag years that puts her in her dotage. She has seen and survived more of what lower Manhattan has had to deliver than practically any other sentient queen around. Anyone who has survived New York in the era that began with Stonewall and ended with the closing of Studio 54 can be forgiven for their affinity for Weimar-style theatrics and civilizations in decline. "I think we had the sense that in that era America, the American Empire, was completely collapsing," she recalls. "You didn't have to spell it with a 'K' anymore." • A precocious preteen queen, Hattie first did drag as a five-year-old in his

M.O.:   Other (Historian)

home in the Riverdale section of New York, where he and his family moved from Yonkers. "For some inexplicable reason," he confesses, "I dressed up as Hitler!" He was apparently unaware of just what kind of guy he was emulating. Hattie remembers that growing up in postwar America in the late fifties and early sixties, kids saw Hitler as simply "the most striking image of power. He was everywhere." Her claims of innocence are belied by the additional memory that for whatever reason dressing up as Hitler "was kind of *verboten.*" But a flair for the perverse has always been one of Hattie's more salient features. By the early- to mid-seventies she was a youthful Greenwich Village regular, hanging out with sainted street queen **Marsha P. Johnson** and soaking up the sexually charged atmosphere of vaunted post-Stonewall clubs and bars that have long since shut their doors. A favorite haunt was the Anvil, where on any given night Phillipe (the "Indian" from The Village People), among others, could be seen wagging his behind on the bar upstairs, while downstairs sex acts that would kill even the most rugged of postmodern sexual athletes were staged round the clock for a generally spaced-out audience. It was the Anvil's New Wave Night that sparked the great age of New York drag that found its epicenter at the Pyramid Club. Hattie went there with it and, inspired by the late, great **Ethyl Eichelberger**, began performing as Loretta Nicks, producing a combo-tribute to two favorite female vocalists of the time (Loretta Lynn and twirling sensation Stevie Nicks). Eventually, he took over management of the club and—after having become famous for staging enormous theatrical extravaganzas—he was known for some time as Loretta B. DeMille. A series of farcical accidents (involving liquor, cash and his grandmother's suitcase) led to a final name change and—as a driving force behind the best of New York drag performance—the name Hattie Hathaway was inscribed in the book of downtown nightlife. • Today, Hattie still thrives on subverting audience expectations, a neat trick when what one expects already is subversive! It's anyone's guess what she'll come up with next. To begin with, in a milieu in which a quick wit and rapid-fire reflexes are generally regarded as indispensable, Hattie has cleaved a path all her own. No one, let alone a drag queen, could be more torpid or sluggish in her speech. She is to drag what Bouley is to cooking. During a recent night at *For Cryin' Out Loud,* an evening which she created, hosted and named after one of her favorite catch phrases, anticipation turned to existential panic as she pulled numbers like taffy in a leaden game of, what else, *Das Bingo.* She may be slow, but she's sincere, and every hour or so another round of woozy winners were collecting their prizes. • Hattie's passion, though, is history, and thankfully she has complemented her clarity of hindsight with a happy surplus of foresight and throughout the years amassed an

| **RAISED IN:** Riverdale | **CAME TO NYC IN:** 1976 | **STARTED DOING DRAG AT:** 23 |

unrivaled collection of artifacts from the many hot spots she's inhabited. **Ethyl Eichelberger**'s costumes, John Sex's briefs, dozens of photos and articles from a time and a place that might otherwise not be believed. Like a character out of *Grey Gardens,* she is somehow still here, an invaluable lockbox of names, dates, anecdotes and ephemera—as concrete a set of artifacts as one is likely ever to find in the world of drag. She harbors plans to document her unique perspective on the history of the nether regions in which she has trafficked for years. And given the depth of her involvement and the scope of her knowledge, let's hope she does.

How did you come up with your name?
"Hattie was my grandmother who whistled birdcalls at meetings of the Daughters of America. Hathaway is of course Miss Jane from *The Beverly Hillbillies,* whom I worship."

Does anything set New York drag queens apart from those in other cities?
"Their diversity, for one thing. And their lack of facial hair."

What's the worst thing about being a drag queen?
"The cost of petroleum products you put on your skin and the way high heels throw your back out of alignment."

What's the best thing?
"You don't have to pay taxes."

EARLY DRAG NAMES: Loretta
Nicks, Loretta B. DeMille

**FIRST SONG. SUNG OR LIP-
SYNCED:** "D-I-V-O-R-C-E"

SISTERS OF THE CLOTH:
Hapi Phace, Tabboo!

MOTHERS: Ethyl Eichelbeger,
John Kelly

IF NOT DRAG THEN: Writing my
book

TUCKS:
☐ YES ☑ NO ☐ SOMETIMES

Plumage

GLAMOUR   CLOWN

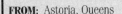

FROM: Astoria, Queens   **SPECIES:**

HEDDA LETTUCE

http:/www. Hedda.com

" *I* had a big mouth," says Hedda Lettuce of her youth. This makes any effort to describe her by definition redundant. There is not another queen who promotes herself so dynamically or relentlessly. Author, columnist, cartoonist, singer, dancer, television star and producer—all are hats worn by this most tireless and industrious worker in the busy honeycomb of drag life in NYC. The last year has seen her rise with almost unprecedented alacrity to the forefront of the drag juggernaut. Call it sheer force of will, dogged persistence or just excess adrenaline, but Hedda has expended an almost superhuman amount of energy putting herself out there. Not unlike most other multifaceted mega-stars, Hedda has a bottomless ambition that seems to stem from a neurotic sense that she can never prove herself adequate, yet is cursed forever to try. The effect this has, odd for a drag queen, is that no matter what risqué burlesque, what outrageous sight gag, what scatological anthem she's performing, there is always the sense that she's been dealing with it in therapy. It is tempting to read her story in purely psychoanalytic terms, but that might be reductive. • Hedda's childhood was characterized by an uncanny sense of alienation from virtually everyone he knew— save his fourth-grade teacher, Mrs. Altman, a "Jewish American Princess" whom he idolized for her slavish devotion to fashion. "She was svelte, had a nose job and wore a white mink coat even in the summer." But perhaps no moment shaped the wan youngster (and his apparent penchant for gals who wear mink) more powerfully than the one in which he describes himself as a "hideous" newborn. "I was supposedly born this horrible color," he recounts. "I was born purple. My father looked at me and said, 'Ooh, what an ugly baby.' As he said this, a

M.O.:

RAISED IN: Same	CAME TO NYC IN: N/A	STARTED DOING DRAG AT: *22*

woman came up behind him, she's wearing a fur coat, and she taps him on the shoulder and goes, 'If you don't want this child, I'll take him because I just lost mine.' And ever since then I've said to myself, 'Why didn't you give me to that woman, you son of a bitch?' She had fashion sense!'" This was not the last time his father would express disappointment with his son's appearance. During Hedda's first attempt at drag (at a precocious eight years old) his father caught him wearing an apron and spinning around the living room, Julie Andrews style, arms in the air, belting out "The Sound of Music." Not at all enchanted by that display, his father growled, "If you want to be a little girl, go ahead and be a little girl," threw the apron at his son and stalked away. • These and other memories are right underneath the surface of Hedda's work, which might explain why even when she is at her funniest, there is always a strange hint of sadness in her gaze. Despite her virtuosity at transforming her features, she has not managed completely to conceal the trauma that is so often the birthright of youngsters doomed to be different. "I remember sitting on the stoop of my house and waiting for someone to come by and discover me and take me away from it all," she recounts, noting that it would be years before she would come to understand the apocryphal nature of those Hollywood-and-Vine stories. She eventually replaced hope with hard work, and wishes with hours of planning and preparation, and she now strives endlessly to maintain her vaunted position as one of the true stars in the DQ firmament • As self-aware as they come, Hedda has an M.O. that's typical of what many see as a trend within drag: performers who turn the mirror on themselves and give you drag about drag. Fond of singing parodies, for example, Hedda translates lyrics to reflect her own experience. In this fashion, "You Ain't Nothing But a Hound Dog"

What is drag?
   "The right wig, the perfect dress, a flawless face."

If your life were a novel, what would the chapter headings be titled?
   " 'I Hedda Dream' or 'I Hedda: Tales of a Drag Queen Warrior.'"

Career Highlights
   Drag Talk, The Hedda Lettuce Show
   Laura Brannigan Video

EARLY DRAG NAMES: Vegina Vagina, Miss Fortune, Miss Conception

FIRST SONG. SUNG OR LIP-SYNCED: "The Man I Love"

SISTERS OF THE CLOTH: Miss Understood

IF NOT DRAG THEN: Construction

TUCKS:
☐ YES ☐ NO ☑ SOMETIMES

Plumage

GLAMOUR   CLOWN

BEEN DOING DRAG FOR: 3 years

becomes "I Ain't Nothing But a Drag Queen" as she reveals the ins and outs of what is otherwise disclosed on a strictly need-to-know basis. • As much-needed comic relief in the otherwise joyless video bars that are spreading throughout Chelsea and the Village, she's been known to sing "I Can't Get Shit Out of My Life" with fellow scat singer **Sherry Vine** or hostess mud-wrestling contests between the Brady girls (including the fourth, unknown sister, Nilda, who was apparently fired after the first pilot for being too "ethnic"—played by **Chicklet**) and those ample coeds from *The Facts of Life*. When she's not refereeing bloody battles between once and future stars of *The Love Boat*, Hedda can also be seen on her own weekly variety show, *The Hedda Lettuce Show*—and, of course, on all the commercials in between. Her art and articles are featured regularly in any number of papers and magazines, and don't forget to call her psychic hotline—it's only $3.99 a minute! • In the end, it would appear that her journey toward some sort of peace with herself and her family is progressing as it should. She happily notes that when her father sat through a recent viewing of her television program, he was delighted. "You're so talented!" he is reported to have said. "All you need is a break!" It may not be quite time to give the shrink her pink slip, though. Hedda's dad went on to note, "Of course, **RuPaul** is prettier."

FROM: Hazlehurst, MS	**SPECIES:**

LYPSINKA
Superstar

*L*ypsinka is one of drag's few genuine stars; a hells-a-poppin', hyperthyroid sparkplug of a dynamo whose manic performances have secured her an international reputation as far more than just a drag queen. It comes as no surprise that she lip-syncs, but as her carefully contrived name/logo suggests, she has reinvented the form, turning tradition on its ear by mouthing (with inhuman precision) insanely complicated, richly layered, often soaring audio montages fashioned together from countless movies, musicals, literature, television and even occasionally Lypsinka's own fertile (if psychotic) imagination. These she stages in strange yet familiar settings—in her signature Dovima meets Dracula ensemble—combining a supernatural energy and sexy fury that recall the best of Ann-Margret, Shirley Bassy and Tyrannasorous Rex. "It's got mother love, it's got musical numbers, it's got realism—such as it is. It's mostly impressionistic but with real moments of expressionism," she says, not about her performance, but about her favorite film, Douglas Sirk's prematurely post-modern masterpiece *Imitation of Life*. There could not be, however, a better description of Lypsinka's own legendary shows, *The Many Moods of Lypsinka, I Could Go on Lip-syncing!* and *Lypsinka Must Be Destroyed!* Like Sirk's magnum opus which brings together such disparate stars as, among others, Lana Turner and Mahalia Jackson, Lypsinka's pieces are bizarre, ironic and slickly crafted—but oddly wrenching in their own way. Lypsinka rummages through the collective psyche, expertly weaving together mnemonic strands both stylish and political, melding the sounds and images of a glamorous, yet hellish time. As such, her peformances have been received with the kind of critical acclaim and high-profile reportage that is reserved for true

M.O.:

stars of the theater . . . which, as she herself will gladly inform you, she is. • But please, don't call him a drag queen! He bristles madly at the very mention of the word. Even though that may be exactly what she is, Lypsinka—or more precisely John Epperson—is singularly keen on avoiding that moniker, preferring loftier labels such as drag "artist," drag "performer" or, if you will, drag "star." With fanatical insistence, Epperson maintains that Lypsinka is a creature of the theater, and that as her creator, every act is tied to a strictly artistic agenda—despite his humble beginnings in the same East Village night spots that nurtured so many of his less well enfranchised colleagues. While he may share the same Pyramid pedigree as many an infamous nightcrawler, Lypsinka is reluctant even to be mentioned in the same breath as, say, Girlina, who regardless of how things might appear from a distance, is about as much like Lypsinka as Norman Rockwell is like Vermeer. • It seems puzzling that someone who has broken as much ground as he, whose work alone has brought him into the bosom of the very stars who first inspired him as a child, who describes hanging out backstage with the likes of Bette Midler, Ann-Margaret, Liza Minnelli and Lily Tomlin, should be as concerned with labels as he is. Skittish and wan, Epperson attributes this persistent paranoia to a lingering sense that drag queens have traditionally been "the lowest part of the totem pole in the gay community, which is what—twenty years ago—the drag queen was. I was afraid people would treat me like trash." Hence the desire to distance himself professionally from the notion, albeit a hoary one, that queens are fundamentally flawed. There is also a hint, however, that unlike most queens, Epperson saw his destiny coming very early in life and that he has been struggling with its potential downside for much longer than most. Whereas many queens don't even try drag until well into their teens or twenties, Epperson remembers how as just a little boy, a child prodigy really, he enjoyed romping around in dresses and frocks, entertaining the ranks of an adoring family. "Once after I did my June Allison impersonation for my mother," he recalls fondly, "after she had very kindly driven me to New Orleans to see a Carmen Miranda movie, she said 'Oh, maybe you can be a female impersonator some day like Jim Baily on *The Carol Burnett Show!* ' " In this way, his extreme caution could be understood as a primal struggle to redeem and transform a childhood fantasy that might otherwise have seemed abject and cursed. • The irony of course is that it is precisely this notion upon which Epperson has built his signature style. He is trapped in a kind of ideological double-bind in which, as a post-modernist performer, he is capitalizing on all the worst stereotypes associated with the drag queen—all the boozing, sobbing, hysterical pathology that he himself most fears—while at the same time trying to avoid being accused of those traits in actuality. It must be a very cramped little space in which to exist, and yet it is precisely where Lypsinka lives and is probably why she enjoys the legitimate popularity that she does. So while it might be tempting to dismiss her position as the rantings of a diva or the unconquered fears of a child, in the end, one can't argue with success. If by denying the label "queen" he has, in fact, forced his audience to view Lypsinka as a purely theatrical entity, then what she's done ain't been in vain. "People think we're frivolous, inconsiderate and silly," lectures Epperson, looking very deer-in-the-headlights. "I don't want people thinking that about me because I do come through, I do deliver the goods, I do show up on time. I want people to want

RAISED IN: Same	CAME TO NYC IN: 1978	STARTED DOING DRAG AT: 24

to book me and to want to see my show. And those who think they can imagine what it's like are wrong . . . I'm very serious about not being serious . . . " he goes on to assert. Imitation of life, indeed.

On how she made it big:
  "I rehearse . . . a lot."

On when she made it big:
  "One night, Elton John came to see my show. That's when I said to myself, 'Something's going on here.' "

Career Highlights
  Her many shows which have run off-Broadway as well as in L.A., San Francisco, and Europe
  Countless print ads, music videos including George Michael's "Too Funky" and the Paris fashion shows
  Meeting Faye Dunaway

EARLY DRAG NAMES: Patti Puke, Mannequin, Cha-Cha Cha, Dee-Dee Dee

FIRST SONG. SUNG OR LIP-SYNCED: "It's Impossible" (sung by Patti Duke in *Valley of the Dolls*)

SISTERS OF THE CLOTH: Charles Busch, RuPaul, The "Lady" Bunny

MOTHERS: Charles Busch, Charles Ludlam, Divine, Craig Russel

IF NOT DRAG THEN: Juvenile Ingenue

TUCKS:
☑ YES ☐ NO ☐ SOMETIMES

Plumage

GLAMOUR   CLOWN

| FROM: Denver | SPECIES: | | |

VARLA JEAN MERMAN

The Big Easy

"*A*ll of my brothers got cars when they were fifteen," says Varla Jean Merman, née Jeff Roberson. "But I didn't get one until much later because my family was scared that I was going to get in the car and drive to New York." And who could blame them—or him for that matter. The son of a peripatetic FBI agent, Roberson lived under the constant threat of having his family uprooted by his father's work. In the ninth grade, facing the possibility of having to leave one Southern small town for another even smaller, he took the drastic step of writing a letter to his mother in which he declared himself to be gay, and went on to protest "that they couldn't move to a smaller town because I had to be with my gay people." To this day his family has no idea that he does drag, let alone that as Varla Jean Merman (the bastard child of Ethel Merman and Ernest Borgnine) he is one of a handful of New York queens who are on the verge of true cross-over success. Here's why: Varla Jean Merman can sing. Her voice alone might be reason enough to reconsider the tradition of lip-syncing which has for so long been in vogue but which is beginning to lose its luster in the eyes of many queens. But, for what it's worth, there are few if any other queens who could on their best night pull off vocally what Varla does during even an average performance. Blessed with a truly enormous range—including a soaring falsetto that is the envy of many female singers—and a goodly dose of honest to god musical talent, she's rediscovering a kind of drag that virtually died out with the advent of high-fidelity portable sound equipment. Her vocal gifts are matched, furthermore, by a wicked sense of humor and a rare talent for extravagant and incisive parody. While some of the songs she sings are her own (and they are often very clever and feature respectable melodies), most are send-ups of the work of established composers such as Anne Murray, Dolly Parton and Olivia Newton-John. A theme, you ask? Why, yes. The "Lesbian du Jour" segment of her traveling feast of musical surprises is to her

M.O.: Other (Nightclub)

| RAISED IN: Same | CAME TO NYC IN: 1993 | STARTED DOING DRAG AT: 21 |

show what Letterman's Top Ten List is to weeknights. • Varla Jean had been doing drag for some time before she landed in NYC. Perhaps that is why her ascent here has been so sudden. In a matter of less than two years, she has starred in her own off-Broadway show, which received considerable critical praise, appeared in many magazine and television features and continues to command the kind of SRO audiences that were otherwise the exclusive purview of such seasoned performers as **Joey Arias** and **Lypsinka**. As a self-starter in the Baton Rouge/New Orleans area, where she was a student at Louisiana State, and where the drag community is about as tolerant of nonconformity as is the Miss America Pageant, Varla made all sorts of waves by entering their highly regimented drag pageants sporting Nurf balls not only in her bra but under her wig as well. Callow as she was, she had yet to learn the fine art of properly teasing a wig. Ironically, her armature high-jinks and nothing-to-lose attitude gained her mountains more notoriety in the well-trussed New Orleans drag community than she ever would have got playing by the rules. It's no surprise then, that, during a trip to New Orleans, New York party promoter Lee Chappell only had eyes for Varla. She had been starring in a friend's crudely produced videos and showing them in local bars. Enchanted, Chappell grabbed her up and took her to New York, where one thing led to another, as they say. A photo shoot for *Details* here, a performance at the Pyramid there, a tour of Europe with teutonic wackster Suzanne Bartsch, and Varla's star was almost instantly on the rise. • Amazingly, while she's consistently one of the busiest drag performers in the city, producing an entire evening's worth of fresh material on a grueling weekly basis, Varla is also one of the only queens who holds down a full-time

On her name:
   "I chose Varla because at the time talk shows kept interviewing these loser relatives of famous people. So I decided to be the loser relative of Ethel Merman who was addicted to laxatives and always trying to be famous."

Career Highlights
   The Man Who Got Away, one woman show off-Broadway
   Mermanschantz, weekly cabaret at Eight-Eights
   Appeared in several layouts, print ads and fashion shoots in various magazines

EARLY DRAG NAMES: Varla

FIRST SONG. SUNG OR LIP-SYNCED: "Free Again"

SISTERS OF THE CLOTH:
   Miss Coco Peru

MOTHERS: None

IF NOT DRAG THEN: Mime

TUCKS:
   ☐ YES   ☐ NO   ☑ SOMETIMES

Plumage

GLAMOUR   CLOWN

job. True, most queens can be seen holding down a sprawling variety of service-oriented gigs (save for those few who prefer the welfare roles) but Varla's got an actual career. She's a professional, recently promoted to creative director in a major advertising firm. • How she manages to pull the whole shebang off is a miracle of modern makeup—but it's not out of character. Roberson recalls somewhat ruefully that not only did his family fear his fierce ambition to escape to New York, but also, in locking down the pastries ("My mother used to keep count of the Little Debbie cakes to see if I had cheated on my diet.") they seemed to sense the extent to which Jeff might otherwise "grow." In denying him the car and the cakes they seemed somehow karmically to know that little Jeff was headed for a kind of greatness that they could only try in vain to control or prevent. Perhaps they knew even before Varla did. Perhaps that's precisely why she's made it so big, why she's having her cake and eating it too, why she can finally say with confidence, "I'm a larger-than-life character. You know, everything about Varla is big."

FROM: Hope, NJ

SPECIES:

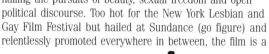

GLENNDA ORGASM
Drag Queen Activist

ℱor Glennda Orgasm, drag is a ploy, political theater, a rhetorical trojan horse. Like **Hapi Phace**, from whom (in a rich moment of gauntlet passing) she received her first wig, Glennda has little use for performing in dance clubs or looking so real that men can't tell the difference. Glenn Belverio, as he is otherwise known, uses drag as a way of engaging in a dialogue, disarming detractors and penetrating the rhetorical barriers that so often prevent people from partaking in an interesting debate. Drag doesn't seem to matter much to Glennda in and of itself, but rather as a means to an end, one which combines artistic ambition, political action and, lest we forget, self-promotion. After all, she notes, "I've always wanted to be a celebrity, and this is the only way I could achieve that." • A veteran of ACT UP, the AIDS advocacy organization that in the late eighties and early nineties fused art, politics, and guerrilla theater to redefine the art of political protest, Glennda coined the term "activist drag." As such, it is a logical extension of the creative, confrontational and often theatrical forms of protest pioneered by that group. Furthermore, she is steeped in the erudite jargon of feminist and queer theory, and is fond of couching virtually all of her work in such academic terms. This may be no accident, for by far her greatest claim to the celebrity she craves has been the two short films she produced, directed and starred in with the undisputed queen of in-your-face postfeminist theory, Camille Paglia. Their hilarious and incendiary collaboration, *Glennda and Camille Do Downtown,* a fifteen-minute tornado of a film, features the two stars as they wander the Village making pilgrimages to gay landmarks, berating anti-porn feminists and hailing the pursuits of beauty, sexual freedom and open political discourse. Too hot for the New York Lesbian and Gay Film Festival but hailed at Sundance (go figure) and relentlessly promoted everywhere in between, the film is a

M.O.:   Other (Film)

classic of the as yet nascent "drag activist" genre, and is a must-see for anyone who still has a sense of humor. It has since been followed up by a worthy sequel, *Glennda and Camille Do Fashion Avenue.* • The success of the films has all but eclipsed Glennda's other contributions to drag and its slow but steady bubbling to the surface of popular culture. *Glennda and Camille . . .* was an offshoot of Glennda's groundbreaking public access television show *The Brenda and Glennda Show,* which she created with her erstwhile partner in public accessibility **Brenda Sexual.** Theirs was the first full-fledged attempt to bring drag to the airwaves and ultimately spawned an entire generation of similarly crudely produced, yet undeniably entertaining shows on public access that are created by and showcase drag performers. • It is evident, however, that even as he struggles to define himself apart from The Collaboration, Belverio's work with Paglia has brought him the most satisfaction. In Paglia, the other man from Hope (New Jersey, that is) has found more than a soulmate or partner in crime, he has found a sort of savior. For Paglia has helped provide not only a vocabulary with which to articulate the issues so dear to him (and with it a measure of intellectual respectability) but more basic forms of support as well. "I believe in the old-fashioned notion of artists having patrons rather than relying on government funding," Glennda asserts with typical didacticism. A rural drag queen with just a high-school diploma, she has succeeded in befriending and collaborating with a leading scholar of her day and, to some extent anyway, raising the level of the discourse regarding the relationship of gender to politics. • Sometimes, however, success can be one's worst enemy. Whereas protest from within the gay community has traditionally been directed outward toward the straight establishment at large, Glennda has trained her sights upon the gay and drag communities themselves, calling for new solutions to difficult problems and radical stances on many sensitive issues. In so doing, she has often

---

Why has drag become so popular?
"It's always been popular. It's resurfaced due to the inadequacy and confusion around male and female gender roles."
How would you advise civilians to start a conversation with you?
"First they should offer to buy me a drink (Vodka martini with an olive). Be polite and upbeat. Compliment me only if you mean it. Don't be afraid to start an argument with me, but be prepared to deal with the consequences."

EARLY DRAG NAMES: Same

FIRST SONG. SUNG OR LIP-SYNCED: "Happy Talk" (from *South Pacific*)

SISTERS OF THE CLOTH: Vaginal Davis

MOTHERS: Camille Paglia

IF NOT DRAG THEN: Film or video

TUCKS:
☑ YES ☐ NO ☐ SOMETIMES

Plumage

GLAMOUR   CLOWN

alienated herself from the one group she was ever likely to be allied with politically. Few other queens count themselves as big fans of Glennda's, perhaps because she insists on pushing buttons even within the narrow confines of the drag realm. Many of the queens whom she did call friend (most of whom got started on early episodes of her show) have forsaken her and won't be looking back anytime soon. But such is the price one pays for making a habit of getting stuck in other people's craws. "One of the reasons why I've stood apart from the drag community . . . is that I'm too political. Even though my politics have evolved. When I first started," she says, "it was sort of a campy offshoot of the sort of politics that were going on in ACT UP and Queer Nation . . . as a form of entertainment to bring issues around the AIDS crisis and queer politics to other audiences, straight audiences or whatnot. But in the past five years I've come to reevaluate some of the political decisions that the gay movement has made. I'm sort of like a rebel now, in and outside of the gay community." If anything, though, she wears that status as a badge of honor, heroically waving her own flag as a courageous and necessary antidote to what she views as the incestuous, watered-down pandering of mainstream gay politics. • With all this talk of alienation, critical theory and political provocation, it is easy to forget that Glennda is also part of a grand tradition of style-mongering, voluptuary extravagance and entertainment. But not to worry; at the end of the day he knows whence he comes and whither she goes. About the two *n*s in Glennda, for example, there's no esoteric philosophy to unravel, no academic treatise to endure. Only a simple maxim that might fall from the lips of the most politically benighted of queens: "If Barbra can lose the *a*, then I can use another *n*!"

| **FROM:** Hawaii | **SPECIES:** |

RAVEN-O
Goddess of Fire

*I*nscrutable as the sphinx, coy as a cat, slippery as a snake, Raven-O is one of New York's most enduring drag legends, a poker-faced diva whose carefully crafted persona seems to reflect all of the mystery, romance and primordial energy of her native Hawaii. A convincing chanteuse who combines the lascivious purring of Eartha Kitt with the gutsy power of Dinah Washington, her singing is an audible metaphor in which her whole story gets told in the microcosm of a song. She simmers, she wails. She is hot—cool on the surface, roiling underneath. She knows whereof she sings. She communicates with the authority of someone who has been around a lot and for a while. In her early thirties, she is already an elder in the drag queen community, a sage-like figure who for many, in particular the veterans of the Boy Bar Beauties, represents as close to a mother figure as any they are ever likely to find. • 'Twas not ever thus, however. The worldly and sedate matriarch one sees now is the product of years of turmoil and extreme behavior that comprise all of the stages of the classic odyssey of the New York Wild Child. Chapter One, which she calls "Outside Looking In," takes place at home as a boy. "I just had to get out of there because I felt like I didn't belong. Someone put me there by mistake." Chapter Two: Enter the Cyclone. "I was a freak, then I left there and came to New York, to the other freaks." In the emerald bosom of New York City, Raven-O ran the gamut gauntlet. She played the punk, the New Wave diva, the pre-op transsexual and even, upon occasion, the freak for hire. (This latter role, difficult as it must have been, she dropped only after she found herself accepting a fee of less than four dollars for one night's work.) When she realized that a full-fledged surgical transformation was not in fact on the docket, when she got it that being a boy could be fun too, she settled on "evening drag" as the logical way to preserve one jewel's multiple facets. "I was really anorexic, skinny and looked like a woman . . . I was going to get breasts . . . I was having a major identity crisis. Then I realized, I was a drag queen!" • She was one of the few personalities strong and stubborn enough ever to face down Boy Bar's resident svengali and autocrat Matthew Kasten on his own ground, and together they spent close to ten years in loco parentis to an entire generation of growing boys and girls. Having watched all her babies fly the coop, having watched even the dissolution of the farm itself, Raven-O has in recent years lowered the volume on an infamously aggressive and

M.O.:

RAISED IN: Same	CAME TO NYC IN: 1985	STARTED DOING DRAG AT: 18

outrageous style of performance. No longer does she shower her audiences with cake flour or hurl empty beer bottles at impudent patrons. Now, often wigless (featuring a sometimes bald and always feminine pate) she appears witchlike in black organza, snapping her long fingers and exhibiting the magnetic quietude that is the property of only those who have walked the long road home. She whispers as she sings. She smiles slyly as she scats. She is, above all, relaxed. Her rendition of "Let's Face the Music and Dance" is more a smoky incantation than a romp through a great American standard. Her "Four Women," a quasipolitical, neospiritual (deftly and subtly parodied by meta-queen Sandra Bernhardt in her one-woman spectacular *Without You I'm Nothing*), is rendered with such earthy sophistication that one has the sense that it was written expressly for Raven. This all makes perfect sense to the self-consciously cool Miss O who has titled this latest chapter of her loopy and intensely lived life "My Voice." "If you lip-sync, you're not going anywhere," she declares, regardless of those lip-syncers in her own circle who seem to be doing just fine. "You also have to be pretty." While technically limited, she manipulates her feline instrument in the grand tradition of song stylists who often have more to offer musically than their equipment allows. If her growing cadre of followers is any gauge, then she is on the right track. • Currently in collusion with one of her all-time favorite queens, Joey Arias, Raven is leading drag into the setting for which it might be best designed: the nightclub. It is the perfect ambience for a performer like Raven. Cabaret audiences have long placed a premium on worldliness and insight borne of experience. This milieu has finally allowed Raven to click her heels and rest a while. Someone once asked her what she found to be the best thing about doing drag. Without missing a beat or moving a muscle she replied, "Everything, baby. Everything."

Why do you do drag?
  "Because I can."

On NY drag scene and younger queens:
  "They are incredible, because they do what they do so well in the short amount of time they have been doing it. There is still something missing from what they do, but that will happen in another five years. You know when you cook something and it simmers for a long time in order to get the flavor perfect. They need to simmer some more."

On drag:
  "Drag is not sexual to me. The only thing that is sexual for me is when I'm performing, but that is about the performance, about being sexy. I'm being sexy."

EARLY DRAG NAMES: Tempest, Stone Baby

FIRST SONG. SUNG OR LIP-SYNCED: "Ain't No Mountain High Enough"

SISTERS OF THE CLOTH: Joey Arias

MOTHERS: Matthew Kasten

IF NOT DRAG THEN: Nothing

TUCKS:
☐ YES   ☐ NO   ☑ SOMETIMES

Plumage

GLAMOUR   CLOWN

FROM: San Diego

SPECIES:

PERFIDIA
The Sultan of Switch

"*F*or me a wig is a trademark," understates Perfidia, who as the proprietress of the "Wig Bar" at Patricia Field's (Eighth Street's counter-couturier to the drag stars) has raised the simple act of teasing a wig into a high (very high) art. She doesn't simply promote and sell wigs, she styles them, molds them, shapes them—loves them, really. As such she has created unforgettable signature hair explosions for virtually every drag queen on the loose. "Barrel curls are my favorite style," she says of the towering confections that resemble everything from luminescent wedding cakes to cascading waterfalls to pre-SALT Treaty ICBMs. Come Labor Day and the annual ritual of *Wigstock,* a business that is never less than brisk becomes a tsunami of eager patrons. For weeks in advance of the event that puts the Hair Club for Men to shame, the bulk of *Wigstock*'s performers come to consult with New York's undisputed Sultan of Switch and order the creations that will crown the ensembles they've spent months preparing. The days and nights blend together as Perfidia slaves over a hot curling iron and mountains of multicolored fibers, struggling to meet a deadline that in recent years has become ludicrous. Meanwhile an increasingly heavy stream of headdress-hungry tourists and casual shoppers come to purchase from Perfidia's extensive and meticulously maintained line of ready-to-wear pageboys, blunt cuts, bobs and afros. • Perfidia's story before she became the wigged-out guru she is comprises all the classic elements of the New York drag queen ur-narrative—and then some. The son of a Marine colonel and a Sicilian coal miner's daughter, he grew up in San Diego, the dismal suburban spur of Los Angeles which Perfidia describes benignly as "boring." For a budding style maven such as she, however, nothing could be more suffocating and she spent the late seventies and early eighties escaping to Hollywood, hanging out at countless

M.O.: Other (Wigs)

RAISED IN: San Diego and VA	**CAME TO NYC IN:** 1988

screenings of *The Rocky Horror Picture Show* and working that "Teddy Boy look to get the boys." Chasing after Adam Ant wishes and Marc Almond dreams, Perfidia occupied his time absorbing the glamour and the hustle of being young, hot and sexually ambiguous in the entertainment capital of the world. "I really just wanted to be beautiful. That was my goal," he says of those illicit nights spent away from home. For his pains, he recalls, his parents locked him up in "a mental institution" for boys. Whatever success he might have had there, however, it wasn't long before, in a fit of romantic antiestablishmentarianism, he and a non-incarcerated boyfriend arranged for a Hollywood-style, fence-leaping, moped-driven escape worthy of any James Dean coming-of-age picture. • Several lives later, after clubbing, hustling and training to be an actor, young Steven scraped together 800 dollars, what was left of his wits, and struck out for New York. The glam/punk look he had worked so hard to develop as a West Coast youth stood him in good stead in New York, where he caught the eye of not a few prominent denizens of the nightlife netherworld, store owner Patricia Field among them. Drag could not be far off. After a youth spent dressing up, getting down and getting out, one Halloween in drag was like falling off a log. He started doing drag as Concha, from the film *The Devil Is a Woman,* the video of which he borrowed from his roommate at the time, drag legend and supermom **International Chrysis**. Perfidia views her, as many queens are wont to, as a genuine mother figure, a nurturing, imaginative source of love and inspiration without whom he might well have lost his way. Other members of Perfidia's adoptive New York family, which reads like a Who's Who of New York drag, include his "godmother," 82 Club legend **Tish,** his "aunt" **Jayne** (née Wayne) **County** and his distant cousin from the old country **Rhome Hog**. Performances with Chrysis and the estimable **Hot Peaches** in Germany ("the first time I was anywhere where drag queens were treated as hot sexy things") and weekly parties at super-promoter Suzanne Bartsch's Copacabana gave Perfidia the notoriety she adored and helped to cement the increasing sense of self she had been developing in New York. Eventually, in a scene of alternative parental consummation, Chrysis, sensing a mistake, rebaptized her under her current sobriquet. • Meanwhile, at the Boy Bar, with old friend and fellow Los Angeline **Miss Guy,** Perfidia helped create a wildly popular scene which defined an era in the world of New York drag. She lip-synced only the vocals of Katerina Valente, a largely unknown Latina

EARLY DRAG NAMES: Concha

FIRST SONG. SUNG OR LIP-SYNCED: "The Breeze and I"

SISTERS OF THE CLOTH: Glamamore, Connie Girl

MOTHERS: Matthew Kasten, International Chrysis

IF NOT DRAG THEN: Actor

TUCKS: ☑ YES ☐ NO ☐ SOMETIMES

Plumage

GLAMOUR — CLOWN

swing singer. Highlighting the drag queen's innate ability to conflate style with substance, she says, "I was collecting records; I saw her hairstyle and knew her records must be awesome." The combination of Perfidia's dead-on, spicy performances, knack for styling wigs and close ties to both Pat Field's and the Boy Bar, created a synergy that turned her into a star and the "Wig Bar"— which she created—into a veritable institution. • Now, remarkably composed for a soul who has seen, and lost as much as he has, Perfidia has ascended to the role of elder statesman of drag. Coolly grooming her wigs and chatting with the endless parade of shoppers and queens that passes through her little magic kingdom, she muses in measured tones about the meaning of life and the nature of the beast whose franchise she's basically come to own. "I love the instant gratification of a wig. That's the basic selling point for me. Here it is, you can have it right now. Who cares what other people think and who cares if it looks fake!" On the contrary, isn't that the point?

| FROM: Atlanta | SPECIES: |

HAPI PHACE
The Philosopher Queen

*H*api Phace looks like a man who's been hit in the head by a wig. Odd for someone who is considered one of an elite core of drag queen elders—legends from the Jurassic eighties, when East Village queens walked the earth with no real predators to threaten their hegemony. Nevertheless, whether it's the current trend toward realness or the hoarier tradition of fierceness, it makes no difference: throw them all out when you're talking about Hapi. "I was never really looking for fame or success. I was looking to work and learn in the theater." Nor does Hapi don the habit out of a love of glamour or a desire to look feminine; he never wanted to lip-sync to the latest disco hits or show off the shapely cut of his jib. On the contrary, he recalls that his first go at drag was not unlike being forced to walk the plank. Obviously prescient, his friends from the newly opened Pyramid, taken by the talent and charisma they'd seen during his butch performances in plays there, hounded him about giving it a go-go. "I was really bombed one night and they convinced me that I should dress up. They told me that I could get money, get tips. 'You go-go dance on the bar and you get paid at the end of the night,' they said. Well, after one or two cocktails, I said 'No.' Three or four, I said, 'Maybe.' After ten or twelve, I said, 'Where's the wig!'" The rest is herstory, as they say, for Hapi caught fire at the East Village hot spot and his legendary flame shows no signs of dimming. • While Hapi emigrated to New York from Atlanta, he predates that other, more infamous group of Atlantans, the Now Explosion and friends **RuPaul, The "Lady" Bunny** and **Flloyd**. His heart, however, belongs to Athens, another city in Georgia, which, while considerably smaller, has proven no less fecund a breeding ground for pop stars and musicians. Hapi was in fact

M.O.:

college roommates with *that* most prolific of alternative rock giants, but invokes a kind of atavistic respect for privacy and Southern respectability when he refuses to go on record about the sexual proclivities of his erstwhile roomy. Suffice to say that they "used to raid Dumpsters together—help each other carry mannequins back home and make mannequin sculptures." You figure it out. At any rate, Hapi eventually sought out New York, anxious to pursue theater and art. The Pyramid presented an almost unique mixture of both and Hapi became a natural member of its bohemian cast of characters, among them his first real New York friends, **John Kelly, Tabboo!** and drag titan the late **Ethyl Eicheberger**. • The lure of free drinks and quick tips may have led Hapi to put on a wig and dance on the bar, but it was fate that turned him into a veritable institution. He had become a hugely popular go-go dancer—in that anti–go-go sort of way. During a management change at the club, several of the older performers persuaded the new bosses to let Hapi graduate to hosting shows, introducing acts and generally emceeing the always zany, often chemically altered proceedings. By late 1982 Hapi's own night, *Whispers,* had become an enormous success. It was perhaps the quintessence of East Village performance art chic. The room itself was alive with creative energy. Drugs and alcohol were everywhere. Movie stars, celebrities, freaks and assorted glitterati showed up in droves, bringing the club the kind of business that allowed performers to pull in several hundred dollars a night. And there at its center was Hapi Phace, dressed in something awful, purposefully screwing up a song, reciting poetry or riffing on current affairs, but always holding forth in his own Dada fashion. "People thought it was actually my club," he recalls, clearly tickled by the memory. • Watching Hapi now, in her frequent appearances with longtime Pyramid comrade **Hattie Hathaway,** is like watching a pair of seasoned vaudevillians, a twisted Burns and Allen, who—despite the fact that the fragile milieu in which they first flourished is crumbling around them—still run through the old routines with gusto, and just a touch of indignation. Those halcyon days

CAME TO NYC IN: 1981   **STARTED DOING DRAG AT:** 24

are squarely in the past, and despite the occasional hungry academic who shows up seeking information for a dissertation, Hapi seems instinctively to know that most of those old times will be forgotten. But having survived them at all has given him a "happy" perspective. Sitting back, dragging— yes, dragging—on a smoke, imagining his life as a three-act play, he lapses into a reverie. "Act I: Young Boy Wants to Become a Nun," he says as a soundtrack begins playing on some phantom jukebox. "Act I, Scene 2: Young Boy Realizes He Can't Become a Nun. Scene 3: Young Boy Grows Up and Becomes a Drag Queen Instead! Act II: Fifteen Minutes of Fame. Act III: The Aging, Wiser More Moderate Queen Sitting Back, Absorbing What Other People Are Doing—Commenting, Becoming a Sage. I consider myself a philosopher, really. I muse on stage. I'm a muser—and amusing."

On earning money as a drag queen:
"I used to do a show where I would get dressed in drag onstage and add up with an adding machine—'eyeliner, $2.95'—and come up with a grand total of like $8,500 for this look alone. And then I'd go around with a collection cup. When I needed high heels, I'd do the Hapi Phace fund for High Heels for the Disadvantaged Drag Queen, and go around and basically beg from my audience. And then I would come back the next weekend and say, 'These are the high heels that you bought me.'"

On her role models:
"In my day it was Judy, Barbra, and Liza—the Big Three. I was Barbra dominant and Judy submissive. Do you practice Judyism? I'm more into Liza myself. Actually, I'm a practicing Merman. I tested positive for the Merm germ."

Career Highlights
Joe Franklin Show 1986, *Whispers* 1983—1988, *Back Door* 1988—1991, *Son of Sam Delilia,* Charles Atlas film on PBS, Karen Finley's Lamb of God Hotel at the Kitchen 1992.

EARLY DRAG NAMES: Charlene, Bev Hills

FIRST SONG. SUNG OR LIP-SYNCED: "Put on a Happy Face"

SISTERS OF THE CLOTH: Elaine Patrice Simpleton, Hattie, Tabboo!, Sister Dimention

MOTHERS: Ethyl Eichelberger

IF NOT DRAG THEN: Truck driving

TUCKS:
☐ YES   ☑ NO   ☐ SOMETIMES

Plumage

GLAMOUR   CLOWN

FROM: Minnesota   **SPECIES:**

LINDA SIMPSON
Mama Mogul

One dares not ask where contemporary New York drag would be were it not for Linda Simpson. In so many ways, so many roads lead back to her. She has been one of drag's busiest promoter/activists since the late eighties, when she began her string of nights at the Pyramid, during which a large percentage of the current crop of stars got their starts. But even before she opened up the world of drag, she was reinventing the way gay men and lesbians looked at themselves and the world around them. • At heart, Linda has always been primarily a provocateuse, a deceptively undemonstrative rabble-rouser whose best work stems from an abiding need to stir things up. It's surprising to learn that someone who is so composed and whose mien is so ladylike could be the mastermind behind such radical institutions as *My Comrade/Sister* magazine or the Pyramid's delirious *Channel 69,* which was also broadcast on Manhattan Cable. And yet it's true. "I thought there was just a real need for it," she explains about her seminal queer 'zine *My Comrade . . .* , which created an entirely new ethos of underground gay culture. "I found the rest of the gay press was so lugubrious! I wanted to create something that reflected the East Village scene." Driven by a raw, cut-and-paste urgency and an unapologetically post-punk esthetic, *My Comrade*—and its upside-down, Siamese distaff *Sister*—rejected virtually every convention established within the realm of gay publishing—including a publisher. Thrown together and Xeroxed by hand, the groundbreaking 'zine firmly established a gay counter-culture with the gay subculture. Theater reviews and mawkish tributes to dead or dying divas were replaced by camp variations on a glam-rock theme and profiles of still-unknown drag queens. Lukewarm reportage and glossy images were replaced by rough-hewn stories of urban gay life and poorly reproduced, unretouched centerfolds of fleshy East Village boys in well-worn underpants. The two nights that Linda created at the Pyramid were natural theatrical extensions of the raw, rebellious ethos established by the 'zine. For that matter, so was Linda herself. "I needed money for the magazine," recalls Les, Linda's male half. "I started holding benefits and I created Linda to spice them up." After all, necessity is the biggest mother of them all. • She is also the drag community's

M.O.:      Other (Emcee)

| **RAISED IN:** Same | **CAME TO NYC IN:** N/A | **STARTED DOING DRAG AT:** 28 |

favorite whipping girl. Becoming a full-fledged member of the drag queen club means learning how instinctively to get laughs at Linda's expense. In the same way that recruits who rush a fraternity (or in this case sorority) must learn a set of secret rituals, and then in time indoctrinate the next round of comers into the same set of rules, incipient queens learn from their elders that Linda's age, career, wigs and stubborn cosmetic maladies are never to be left well enough alone. She takes it in stride, however, and is not without her own well-stocked arsenal of neutron-style devices. One of the great masters of the shady remark, Linda has a special way of strafing her opponents, silent but deadly. With Linda, unlike many a bitchy queen, neither her tone nor her tempo changes when she is delivering her incendiary payload. By the time the victims of her priceless canards realize they've been soaked in boiling oil, Linda's already halfway down the block, stealthily slipping the boot into her next victim. She is beloved. • Of late, Linda could be accused of becoming the very establishment she once held in such contempt. *My Comrade/Sister* has gone the way of Halley's comet while Linda herself has eschewed the hard work and exclusively personal rewards of staging weekly shows at the ramshackle Pyramid for what she herself has described as the "drag welfare mentality" of hostessing at the slick, monster clubs—all of which are owned, plantation style, by one corporation. But who can deny the benefits of money and relatively easy work for the paid party girl? Not Linda Simpson. In her own way, however, she continues to support up-and-coming queens, which is perhaps appropriate as she takes on the mantle of doyenne. Her articles appear in a number of magazines, including *OUT,* one of the largest-selling legit gay-interest magazines in the world, and she is a "correspondent" for several cable shows geared toward both a young and a gay audience. That the creator of *My Comrade . . .* finds herself hunkering down with the sort of establishment institutions that inspired her to pipe up in the first place is at once ironic and the natural next step for someone who has both broadened the discourse and survived to tell the tale.

How/why did you begin?
"Peer pressure."

What's the best thing about being a drag queen?
"It's very liberating to experience the world from a totally different perspective."

EARLY DRAG NAMES: Same

FIRST SONG, SUNG OR LIP-SYNCED: "Money" (Flying Lizards)

SISTERS OF THE CLOTH: Bunny, Lola, Flloyd, Tabboo!, Paige

MOTHERS: Hapi Phace

IF NOT DRAG THEN: Freedom and happiness

TUCKS:
☑ YES ☐ NO ☐ SOMETIMES

Plumage

GLAMOUR — CLOWN

FROM: Antigua	SPECIES:

TINA SPARKLES

The Gentle Giant

$\mathcal{C}$onfucius once said that he who does not exceed his master, fails his master. If this is so, then Tina Sparkles has certainly triumphed as an eager disciple of parental pedagogy. She hails from the Caribbean island paradise of Antigua, where her mother was a dancer and model who passed her love of physical beauty on to her youngest son. Larry took up the glamour gauntlet with not a little gusto and, as is apparent, eventually eclipsed his mother's undeniably local renown as a great beauty. • An amazon even among drag queens (she describes her family as "a bunch of giants"), Tina glides more than she sparkles, really. She's surprisingly laconic, and her intimidating stature belies a strange sweetness. It is disorienting, after marshaling up the courage to approach this living piece of architecture, to hear the gentle tones of her appreciative voice. A character of this size and scope should, by all rights, breathe fire or spit nails, but instead she smiles and demurely accepts whatever interest people might have in her work. Her whisper reveals a shy introvert, a loner who is far from alone when she expresses the therapeutic effects of doing drag. Movie buffs will recognize her name from the quintessentially Australian cross-over hit movie *Strictly Ballroom;* she appropriated it from a particularly glittery character in that film, after months of laboring under less appropriate aliases given her by the many Svengalis who apparently knew a good thing when they saw it. • Tina's search for her proper name reflects her difficult search for herself, for a sense of rightness and a place that might allow her, like a gargantuan Cindy-Lu Hoo, to raise her voice against the tide of others that would have drowned hers out. For so splendid was Tina's drag that from the moment she crossed the line Halloween night in 1990, she attracted a horde of eager mentors. Party- and self-promoter Suzanne Bartsch was the first to see Tina's potential—and she was willing to pay cash. Before her first night in full regalia had come to a close, Tina had gone from timid twirler to professional personality. • Bartsch was not the only hungry impresario licking her chops over the remarkably ingenuous Ms. Sparkles. Others came, sniffing like dogs, eager to remake this gentle giant in their own images. Because the natural development of the alter-ego should be as organic as that of the (generally) primary self, such attentions can be as destructive as they are inspiring. Labels were hung around Tina's neck like chains. Eager to please, Tina accepted them all, but deep inside she knew

M.O.:

RAISED IN: Same	CAME TO NYC IN: 1990	STARTED DOING DRAG AT: 18

only the pain of invisibility. Who was she really? Pocherser, Caution Larré? Close but no cigar. Such yellow brick roads, however, are unavoidable Rubicons for virtually all such premenarcheal protagonists. For Tina, redemption came in the form of that otherwise innocent Aussie movie rental one fateful night in Brooklyn. When her namesake appeared on the screen, Tina says she "just knew it. That was me!" She put down her knitting and took up her eyeliner. In one crystalline moment, she got her name, her look and her bearings. She was able to face the night alone. • Now, towering over the other revelers on the catwalk at Webster Hall, Tina pierces through the veils that separate the stage from the runway with all the inexorable sashay of a force of nature or a hardened supermodel. And she knows it. She's payed her dues in front of the mirror. She's worked tirelessly to shape her eyebrows to match the coy arch of "Naomi's," to color her lips so they protrude like "Christie's" and to work her mascara just like "Linda's," capturing that unmistakable Dior slant of the upper lid. Taking advantage of her alarming seven-foot profile, she commands whatever space she inhabits, making the other eager beavers vogueing at her knees look like the tugboats that escort great luxury liners to the edge of the ocean. Her smooth gait and sly smile exude all the self-possession that is the hard-won birthright of the movie queen/shop girl who scrimped and saved and scratched her way to the top. One can almost hear strings as she swivels on her spikes and saunters down the catwalk. The crowd can't help but cheer this triumphant heroine of her own epic poem. Tina Sparkles after all.

Why did you come to NYC?
  "I just didn't fit into the island life. I wanted glamour and excitement."

Did you start doing drag before you arrived?
  "After I arrived in New York I discovered high heels and high hair."

If someone wanted to start doing drag, what would be the first thing you
  would tell them to do?
"Learn to walk in pumps and get ready for the drag race because it's a lot of
  work."

Career Highlights
  Developing her own makeup line
  To Wong Foo, Thanks for Everything, Julie Newmar

EARLY DRAG NAMES: Pocherser, Caution Larré

FIRST SONG. SUNG OR LIP-SYNCED: "The Winner in Me" (Patti Labelle)

SISTERS OF THE CLOTH: Tori, Krylon

MOTHERS: Monique Allen

IF NOT DRAG THEN: Makeup

TUCKS:
☑ YES ☐ NO ☐ SOMETIMES

Plumage

GLAMOUR   CLOWN

FROM: N/A   **HABITAT:**

SWEETIE
Big-Titted Honkey Soul Mama

*T*he evangelical quality of Sweetie's work is likely a by-product of her having grown up in a rich Southern Christian tradition. A night with Sweetie is always a night under the tent. And while you'll not hear her preach the tenets of her fundamentalist background, she will give you religion nonetheless. Never nasty, always cheerleading, she is earthy, maternal and large. She's doubtless tired of the comparison, but there is much about Sweetie that is reminiscent of Bette Midler at her ribald best. Mixing heavy doses of sentimental optimism, raunchy humor and burlesque physical humor, Sweetie casts shadows of what it might have been like all those years ago, when Bette and Barry were regulars in the Ansonia Baths, presiding over the debauchery and providing the campy soundtrack to a hedonistic fantasy that would one day turn pitch-black. Devoted to work and thoroughly disciplined, she never gives anything less than her best. She'd rather skip a gig altogether than come up short on the sauce. "Sweetie is not a sloppy kind of queen," she says, à la Colin Ferguson. "Even with her size, she's put together." • "I used to play dress-up as a little boy," she recalls impishly. "I would be Samantha, I would be Jeannie," she says without a trace of doubt that we too are on a first name basis with these characters. "I started watching drag in dumpy bars at about sixteen years old. I looked at the performers as 'bad girls'—hard appearance, vulgar mouths, but showmanship that could bring down the house every Saturday night." Despite these (what should have been) dead giveaways, or perhaps because of them, Daniel—as he is also known—didn't come out of

M.O.:

RAISED IN: N/A	**CAME TO NYC IN:** 1990	**STARTED DOING DRAG AT:** 25

the closet until his mid-twenties. "My friends and I, all theater freaks, would sneak out of the suburbs and race to the city to witness the spectacle. Drag was never a desire of mine at the time, but it did open my eyes to self-creation and the magic that high heels and higher hair could create." • Her New York career began with a brief stint at the Pyramid, where she was "very conservative in A-line dresses and a Sassoon bob." A rare case of a queen who couldn't find her own voice amid the artsy individualism of the Pyramid, she transferred, in effect, to the more structured Boy Bar. When the Boy Bar Beauties got ahold of her, she was "suddenly surrounded by these over-the-top gorgeous creatures. They made a silk purse out of a sow's ear," says the big-boned scion of glamour and unsolicited advice. She adds, "I don't get a sexual thrill from being in drag, but when I'm corseted—you know, there are times when I wear a corset that takes me in ten inches—I have to say that it's almost like a high. Something that could be really agonizing—a change of breathing, a change of posture—is very exhilarating . . . I'll never forget the reaction of the audience the first time I came on stage 'glamorous.' It became an addiction." • Let it also be known that Sweetie is one of the best lip-sync artists in the business. She is smart enough only to perform those recordings that speak to her on a deep emotional level, and the payoff is enormous. So completely does she throw herself into songs—typically the pop-gospel anthems that made Midler a star—that one can actually imagine that it is she who is singing as she mops her brow, tosses herself to her knees and even cries when the moment is right. It is during these testimonial performances that one understands what she means when she talks about her fundamentalist background, saying "I've tried to shake it, but I can't." Her religious upbringing might explain not only her fervency on-stage, but also her reluctance to engage in the sorts of bitchy banter and backbiting that are so often associated with drag. "Being quippy and being able to protect yourself onstage is very important—but not for its own sake . . . Leave the bitchiness to the other girls. Not to say that I'm not a bitch, but it's out of the audience's sight and only when provoked. My acidity is always in fun, not in slander." • Ultimately, Sweetie is all about the show. She describes herself as "the type of girl who would entertain the troops in war-torn countries." She refers to herself almost always as "Mother." "Mother is the ultimate mother. Give, give, give. Always supportive, always willing to sacrifice . . . This is show business so I don't go too far, but kindness is definitely a part of me." That this is true is evidenced by a remark she made regarding one of New York's most popular and difficult queens, one who has never spared Sweetie the rod.

When asked to describe how it feels to be "read" by **The "Lady" Bunny** onstage (a feeling virtually every drag queens knows), Sweetie lovingly sidesteps the question altogether, preferring to focus on what makes Bunny as great as she is. "I think what's so genius about her is you can look at Bunny and realize everything she thought was beautiful as a little kid . . . . If you look at her she looks like Barbara Eden, grown up." Caveat: this is from the man who also said, "A good drag queen is capable of making the unbelievable believable."

Career Highlights
   To Wong Foo...
   Tours of Europe, Amsterdam, Brussels, London
   Photos in galleries
   DQMTV, cable show

EARLY DRAG NAMES: Cousin Gurt
   Munson, Lesbian Authoress

**FIRST SONG. SUNG OR LIP-
   SYNCED:** "Stand by Your Man"

SISTERS OF THE CLOTH: Faux Pas,
   Babe Duke, Randella

MOTHERS: Glamamore

IF NOT DRAG THEN: Schoolteacher

TUCKS:
☑ YES   ☐ NO   ☐ SOMETIMES

Plumage

GLAMOUR   CLOWN

FROM: Worchester, MA	**HABITAT:**

TABBOO!
Drag's Daffy Duck

"*It's* natural!" squawks Warner Brothers recording artist Tabboo! as she half saunters, half stumbles across the Pyramid stage. "For a fag/To do drag/It's natural!" she continues, lip-syncing to her own voice as it spins off the soundtrack of *Wigstock The Movie*. Less a battle cry than a series of rap-infused hiccups, Tabboo!'s signature declaration is followed inevitably by a knowing "Hello!" The crowd, a well-oiled machine designed to respond in kind, enthusiastically gives Tabboo! her props, and drag's zaniest practitioner is off and running—literally. • Erstwhile puppeteer and internationally recognized painter, he came to New York from the New Wave scene in Boston just in time to catch it again in New York as it crested during the early eighties. His combined interest in art, punk, theater and that wide-ranging rubric "glam" made Tabboo! a natural candidate for the Pyramid. A daughter of that club's queen mothers, **Ethyl Eichelberger** and **Tanya Ransom**, Tabboo!'s wacked-out blend of theatricality, sophisticated visual style and gender dysphoria have come to represent the essence of East Village "individualist" drag. Considered by many to be an elder statesman of that tradition, Tabboo! has patented a wacky schtick that might be one of the longest-running shows in New York theater history; if the Alphabet needed its own Lady Liberty, Tabboo! might well serve the turn. • Watching her perform is like watching television while someone else is surfing the channels: allusions to culture, both pop and otherwise, are belched up rapid-fire, in no discernible order, and to no apparent end.

M.O.:	

RAISED IN: Lester, MA	CAME TO NYC IN: 1982	STARTED DOING DRAG AT: Always

Monologues lapse into raps, which in turn give way to songs, which themselves contain elements of dance and literature, history and theater. Had Alice Cooper retooled his look for a show at Disney World and Shari Lewis rethought her routines to play after hours in some Weimar dungeon, the combination of the two might come close to the special dynamism of Tabboo!'s gestalt. • Bearing a cubist resemblance to his half-Armenian sister/idol Cher, Tabboo! defies most conventional modes of drag, including the so-called "clown drag" with which she would seem at first to be most closely allied. Unmistakably East Village, she doesn't tuck in the strictest sense of the word, nor does she fret about issues of realness or beauty. On the contrary, as any great artist is wont to do, Tabboo! delights in turning society's mores and conventions upside down, shaking out the contents and applying them like lipstick to any person, place or thing within arm's reach. To this end, she blends elements of "Goth" and Barbie to create a look that is part Morticia Addams, part Josie and the Pussycats and that sends newcomers reeling, devotees into orbit and idealogues back to the drawing board. "Drag is about using a preconceived notion of what a woman is supposed to be (usually developed by men)—vulnerable or sex objects—and having gay men wear it. It's a male fantasy anyway so why make women wear it?" Incredibly, where Tabboo! is concerned, that's only half the story. • The truth is that Tabboo! is just plain artsy. Intellect and irony all come through loud and clear in an eclectic whirlwind of performance that is as much about the idea of drag as anything else. His openness and approachability, not to mention the simple appeal of his work, has made him one of New York's most celebrated cross-over successes. His paintings hang in museums and galleries around the

Career Highlights
Wigstock The Movie and soundtrack.
Howard Stern's PPV New Year's Eve 1994, with J. W. Bobbit and the Bee Gees
The Love Ball, with Cindy Crawford, House of Willie Wear
Steven Meisel for *Interview,* with Verushka, Christy T., Dennis Hopper, Linda Evans.
RuPaul X-mas Special, with Fred Schneider, Nirvana, Eartha Kitt, LaToya Jackson
Crowned Miss Channel 69

EARLY DRAG NAMES: Pop Up Puppet Theater, Gig Stevens, Popcorn

FIRST SONG, SUNG OR LIP-SYNCED: "Kooky East 6th Street"

SISTERS OF THE CLOTH: Ethyl, Raspberry, Jimmy Paulette, Hapi Phace

IF NOT DRAG THEN: What?

TUCKS:
☐ YES   ☐ NO   ☑ SOMETIMES

Plumage

GLAMOUR   CLOWN

country, he has walked the catwalks of major fashion shows and his visage—which somehow manages to be both glamorous and anti-glamorous at the same time—has been photographed by the likes of superstar photographer Steven Meisel. • So what does a seasoned superstar like Tabboo! make of his success and the pressure of fulfilling the many demands of his own fervent catholicity? "It's all show biz, you know," he responds, like the warhorse he will soon become. And how does he do it? No need to ask of course. It's natural!

| **FROM:** Levittown | **HABITAT:** | |

MISS UNDERSTOOD
Cover Girl

"*I* am not a clown," says Miss Understood with a perfectly straight face. *Oui, et ce n'est pas une pipe!* Perhaps not, but either way, she is different from you and me. Maybe it is because she is from Levittown that Miss Understood strives so hard not to conform. For who would have dreamed that out of the ashes of that nightmare of suburban banality and corporate/domestic uniformity would rise a figure whom even the Drag Queens of New York find scary? "That ain't no drag queen, that's a six-foot Crayola box!" marvels one of Miss Understood's friends and colleagues. "Maybe Miss Understood is actually trying to be pretty and just can't!" opines another who has less to lose. In point of fact, she is neither misguided nor ugly, she is but the quintessence of a highly specialized subcategory within the profession known as Clown Drag—all assertions to the contrary notwithstanding. Day-Glo makeup over pale foundation, neon fabrics and headdresses designed to cause blindness and vertigo, twelve-inch heels and impossibly extended posterior—these are the tresses and accouterments that have made Miss Understood one of the most sought-after and, perhaps a bit ironically, misunderstood of the ranking members of New York's drag elite. Furthermore, underneath the mountains of artifice and madcap Bozo-isms there lives one of the keenest observers of gender play's odd effects on the world at large. Also, she is one of the first (and most industrious) New York queens to tap into the business end of mainstreaming drag, putting a measure of control back in the hands of the players themselves. • The son of a German Jewish cake decorator (which might well explain her penchant for baked-Alaskan head gear) she is neither graceful like **Girlina**, vampy like **Varla**, nor old like **Linda Simpson**. In fact, given the excess of clothing and makeup she dons for work, Miss Understood is oddly untransformed by her drag. Her tendency to clonk rather than strut in those

| **M.O.:** |  |

RAISED IN: Same	**CAME TO NYC IN:** N/A	**STARTED DOING DRAG AT:** Early twenties

twelve-inch Vivian Westwood knockoffs, to speak in the same nasal twang in or out of drag and forgo most of the snaps, crackles and pops generally associated with queens is a reflection of Miss Understood's more anthropological agenda. "Drag to me is taking on certain characteristics that are *attributed* to women. Yes, I wear the corset and the tits because I love the transformation of this character, but I never walk around thinking I'm a girl." It's clear that it is the *idea* of drag that is as interesting as anything for Miss Understood. Taking a cue from her primary role model, the irreducible **Hapi Phace,** she highlights the ridiculousness of being ridiculous. "I was amazed by **Hapi Phace**. I had only seen a few drag shows in my life and I'd never seen someone deconstruct it so much. I mean Hapi looked nothing like a woman. He looked like Herman Munster. He completely made fun of the idea of lip-syncing. He would lip-sync to ridiculous things and he would take off his clothes and lip-sync in a sheer thing, kind of fat and naked. He made a big joke of it . . . Hapi made me want to do drag." • And do it he did. He began by staging "drag-a-thons" to benefit the gay activist organization Queer Nation in Sheridan Square at the heart of Greenwich Village. Under the aegis of longtime acquaintance **Glennda Orgasm,** he and friend **Hedda Lettuce** appeared on Manhattan's infamous system of public access cable channels. Eventually, he found work go-go dancing and DJing at clubs throughout the East Village. All of which would eventually lead him to create his own Saturday night extravaganza at the Pyramid, on the very stage where he had first seen his muse Hapi, making the circle complete. During the day, however, Miss Understood, like many queens, was holding down a dreary job making money for the "Man"—dressing windows at Macy's—and getting little but humiliation and a laughable wage for his pains. It was not long before the dissonance between the joy of drag and the drudgery of his day job forced him to make a decision. He would make his money where his mouth was. "I started *Screaming Queens* because I hate large corporations and big capitalism. I couldn't stand being a slave to my work during the day and not being appreciated for it. Now I control my business and I work with people I like." As the demand for edgier types increases, so does the business. To date, Miss Understood and his circus of stars have appeared in countless television talk shows, commercials and feature presentations. He delights in seeing to it that the wealthy producers who create the programming provide his clients with all of the perks and

EARLY DRAG NAMES: None

FIRST SONG. SUNG OR LIP-SYNCED: "Lord's Prayer" (Nina Hagen)

SISTERS OF THE CLOTH: Hedda Lettuce

MOTHERS: Hapi Phace, Olympia

IF NOT DRAG THEN: Something artistic

TUCKS:
☑ YES ☐ NO ☐ SOMETIMES

Plumage

GLAMOUR · CLOWN

benefits that any performer would expect, but which drag queens have found themselves denied in so many instances. • For someone who was first attracted to drag because of its jokier qualities, Miss Understood has made quite a life for herself. But a peek below the surface of her thickly applied veneer reveals that it's not all box office and ironic distance. While she's quick to spew well-practiced dogma such as "It's all about imagery," or "I like to be balanced so I don't look only like a clown," she eventually reveals what must be true for anyone who endures the rigors of a transformation as gothic as hers: "I like the corset and the legginess. People do tell me I have nice legs."

FROM: Kentucky

SPECIES:

LILLY OF THE VALLEY

Ingenue

"*P*eople tell me I have a certain childlike quality, which they really like." Indeed, skipping around the dance floor at Squeezbox, the red-hot club where she shares hostess duties with the indomitable **Misstress Formika,** sipping on what looks suspiciously like a Shirley Temple, Lilly of the Valley resembles a tyke who has raided her mummy's closet and is playing house with two hundred or so unkempt punk rockers. It's not that she's wearing rompers and rolling a hoop. On the contrary, her leather togs and Tina Turner wig/sculpture are the uniform of a warm leatherette if ever there was one. It is the flighty air of virginity that follows her, even as she screams into the mike or French kisses Hollywood starlets, that contributes to her unspoiled quality. • A graduate of UC Santa Cruz and NYU's Tisch School of the Arts, Lilly is drag's tabula rasa. Unlike most other queens of note, she represents nothing in particular. There is an absence of archness, an unplanned quality about her that suggests that performing in drag was maybe just an accident. Had it been raining one afternoon some years ago, or had a phone rung just a minute earlier, she might just as easily have pursued law or politics—two of her other long-standing interests. • So why drag? It appears that it was a combination of oedipal rebelliousness, theatrical ambition and sexual awakening. The son of conservative parents in a hippie town, he remembers that "when I first came out, I had suppressed so much, I hated men and I identified with women. So when I played a role, I wanted to play a woman." And so he did. In fact, Lilly is really just a character created for a production at NYU who eventually found her way across the footlights. In that play, Michael (Lilly's boy name) played all of the characters, including the protagonist, a young boy who burns down an apartment building. Lilly's character was a tenant to whom an angel spoke. Hers was, therefore, the natural candidate for redemption from the confines of the fictional world. She passed through the fourth wall. "She metamorphosized into whatever I wanted her to be." • There were perhaps more practical reasons for keeping Lilly alive. "After I graduated, I didn't want to be just

M.O.:

| **RAISED IN:** California | **CAME TO NYC IN:** N/A | **STARTED DOING DRAG AT:** 11 |

sitting around waiting for auditions. This way I've been creating some good work, working with some brilliant and hilarious people and having a great time." The nascent quality of his drag leads one to wonder which direction he'll eventually go in. "Listen, so far the best things that have happened to me, the things that have been the most fun, have been completely unplanned." Meanwhile "I've learned how to handle myself around crowds and how to be more outgoing. I'm more confident about my masculinity now than I ever was before. When someone says to me, 'You're an actor,' I say, 'No, I'm a drag queen.' And if they say, 'You're a drag queen,' I say, 'No, I'm an actor.' I don't know if that's just some way of having to avoid being really great at one thing, or if it means I'm a person who's interested in a variety of things. I like that people don't know really what to make of me." In emulation of one of her favorite predecessors, David Bowie, she submits, "I don't want to be pigeonholed. I just want to have fun." • So there she is: New York drag's beautiful blank slate. Smart, talented, lovely to look at with no real axe to grind or agenda to fulfill, she seems uninterested in digging too deep for reasons or justifications. Some time ago she said she felt that the impetus for doing drag was pain. She felt that was true for most people. Now she laughs at the very thought. Strange. Politically alert and immersed in current events, her otherwise dormant dander finally picks up when the subject turns to politics. "During the Reagan years, hate crimes and attacks on gays rose by eight hundred percent, and he didn't even say anything about gay people. It's the tone that he set. It's the sensitivity of the nation. I think it's really important to our lives that we don't have these monsters running the country." If only that phone had rung a few minutes earlier . . .

What's the difference between masculinity and femininity?
"I could write a book."

Who is the most important drag queen working in NYC today?
"Fran Lebowitz."

On misogyny:
"Certainly *some* drag is misogynistic. Do you think women sit around in their apartments and put on makeup all day? We live in a society that hates all things feminine: men are beating their wives up, women are oppressed all over the world, and gay men are hated because of the hatred of women."

On the gay community:
"In the last couple of years the gay community has accepted drag more as the straight community has. But I remember such hurtful things like drag queens not being welcome in parades. I'm sure every drag queen has said that they were so excited to come out and be a part of the gay community and then they found that they didn't belong to it. It is a very common thing. These are the people that are the core of it. The first brick at Stonewall was thrown by a drag queen."

Career Highlights
The Electric Urn, Independent feature also starring Miss Guy
New York Undercover, Fox Television
The Evaporation of Gay Woman, Mabov Mines
Mabov Mines World Tour
God Shave the Queen, drag music compilation on Suroon Records

EARLY DRAG NAMES: Cookie, Willie of the Valley

FIRST SONG. SUNG OR LIP-SYNCED: "Lady Stardust" (David Bowie)

SISTERS OF THE CLOTH: Sherry Vine, Miss Guy

MOTHERS: Antony, Misstress Formika, Flloyd

IF NOT DRAG THEN: Congress

TUCKS:
☐ YES ☐ NO ☑ SOMETIMES

Plumage

GLAMOUR   CLOWN

FROM: Florida | **SPECIES:**

SHERRY VINE

The Ur-Queen

*I*f there were a single drag performer who embodied all of the qualities that other queens themselves find important; one girl who possessed all of the talent, looks and pizzazz that are otherwise rationed out equally among the different performers; a single star who could be called, in other words, the "perfect" New York drag queen, she would be a lot like Sherry Vine. Given the vast array of gifts and the multitude of styles boosted and espoused by her various colleagues, this is no easy feat. Furthermore, notice the strict lines that queens tend to draw between what's good and what's better (not to mention what's bad and what's worse) then marvel at Sherry's unique ability to please virtually every constituency. Club Queens adore her full-throttle sex appeal, sartorial ingenuity and go-for-broke highjinks. Theater Queens know that the elaborate theatrical pageants in which she stars (and which she often writes) plant her firmly in a grand tradition established by **John Vaccaro** and **Charles Ludlam** and carried on by the likes of **Everett Quinton** and **Charles Busch**. Cable Queens and Impresarios need a talent like hers to make their shows sizzle. Singers know that her training in the musical theater makes her a true vocal contender, while fans of lip-sync will tell you she can lip it with the very best of them. Perhaps the only context in which Sherry is less than prodigiously talented is the dance, and yet even there, like all great comedians, she is quick to turn a deficit to her advantage. The only question, then, is why is a performer of Sherry Vine's high caliber not becoming a star as quickly as are some other queens of less? • The answer, ironically, is the same as the question: Keith Levy. Sherry's male counterpart, a veteran of years of legitimate theatrical training, holds a Master's degree in Theater from USC. His is a talent that was perhaps not meant to be funneled exclusively into drag, and therefore his heart may not be in it all the way. This is evidenced clearly by the sophisticated "double-drag" in which Levy is by definition engaged while in the guise of Sherry Vine, herself an actress with ambitions of her own. To watch Sherry over the years has been to watch a hard-bitten, working-class girl from the trailer parks of some nameless mid-Atlantic state struggle to make it to the top of that business they call "show." And while Levy is clearly a gifted character actor, Vine is not. A testament to her lovable lack of talent (and Levy's surplus) is

M.O.:

RAISED IN: Baltimore	**CAME TO NYC IN:** 1991	**STARTED DOING DRAG AT:** 24

the fact that whether she's appearing as a feline serial murderer in Levy's own *Kitty Killer,* as Lucretia Borgia in a passion parody or as a sexy, psychic supermodel plagued by visions of violence, she's still Sherry Vine: singing a little too loudly, acting a little too earnestly and returning all too often to the theme of excrement. It cannot be an easy feat always to approach a character through the filter of this secondary ego; however, this is precisely what Levy has been doing to huge acclaim for the last five years—whether he likes it or not. • An unlikely import from Baltimore, a city that—without a hint of irony—dubbed itself alternately "Charm City," "The Lady by the Bay" and "The City That Reads," Sherry is more easily understood as a native of that same city whose prodigal son, filmmaker John Waters, has named it the "Hairdo Capital of the World." Levy describes a typically trying youth in which his precocious proclivity for fashion had him sashaying around high school in Sergio Valente jeans, cowboy boots and permed hair. This did not make for a smooth journey through adolescence, but by the time graduation came around, his long-standing commitment to his own difference, as well as his excellence in the theater, had garnered him considerable collegial respect and, much to the confusion of his mouth-breathing classmates, popularity with the ladies. Hmmm. • Years ago, after Sherry had finally stopped appearing as the returning champion in **Mona Foot**'s *Star Search,* where she dominated the weekly competition for months on end, Levy mentioned that he had no intention of doing drag for long. It was, at the time, a good way to make money and keep up his theatrical chops. Years later, his drag star has only continued to rise, however, in spite of the sometimes frustrated actor underneath. What may not be great for Levy, though, has been wonderful for drag, since he has moved the mountain of legitimate theatrical enterprise closer to the Mohammed of a truly creative life in drag in New York.

*Why do you think straight
  people enjoy drag?*
  "Everyone loves a clown."

*What about gay and lesbian
  people?*
  "Everyone loves a clown."

*How are you different from
  other drag queens in New York?*
  "I'm cheaper."

What is the meaning of life?
  "Hooch."

Career Highlights
  Kitty Killer, at PS122
  New York magazine cover story
  Scream, Teen, Scream!, movie
  Theatre Couture

EARLY DRAG NAMES: Just Plain
  Sherry

**FIRST SONG. SUNG OR LIP-
  SYNCED:** "Black Coffee"

SISTERS OF THE CLOTH: Candis,
  Misstress, Jackie Beat

MOTHERS: Raven-O, Bobby Miller

IF NOT DRAG THEN: Acting

TUCKS:
  ☐ YES   ☐ NO   ☑ SOMETIMES

Plumage

GLAMOUR ——→ CLOWN

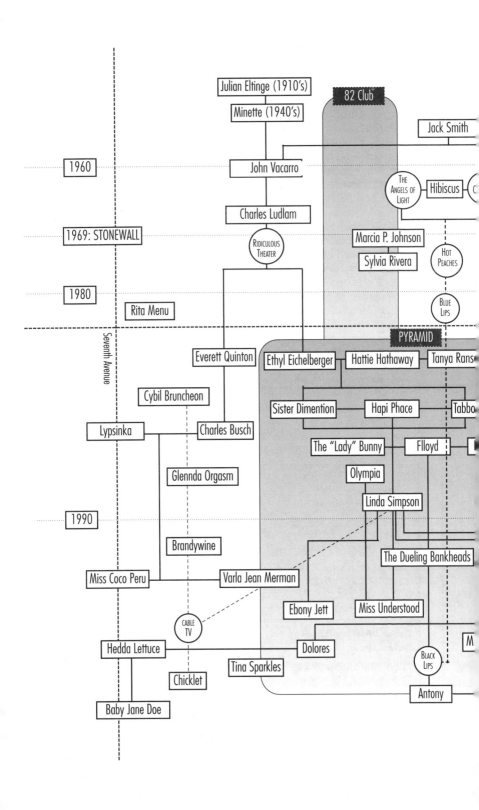

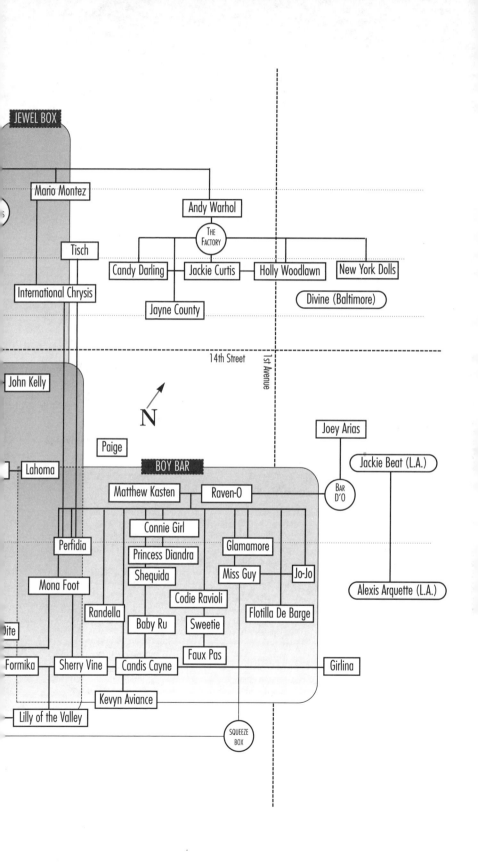

JEWEL BOX

Mario Montez

Andy Warhol

THE FACTORY

Tisch

Candy Darling — Jackie Curtis — Holly Woodlawn — New York Dolls

International Chrysis

Divine (Baltimore)

Jayne County

14th Street

1st Avenue

John Kelly

N

Paige

Joey Arias

Jackie Beat (L.A.)

Lahoma

BOY BAR

Matthew Kasten — Raven-O

BAR D'O

Connie Girl

Princess Diandra

Glamamore

Perfidia

Shequida

Miss Guy — Jo-Jo

Mona Foot

Codie Ravioli

Flotilla De Barge

Alexis Arquette (L.A.)

Randella

Baby Ru

Sweetie

)ite

Faux Pas

Formika — Sherry Vine — Candis Cayne

Girlina

Kevyn Aviance

Lilly of the Valley

SQUEEZE BOX

Index